Contents

GA

Legal and management

The contents of this chapter should be read and used in conjunction with guidance contained within Section A.

Contents

GA

GA01 Health and safety policy

Health and safety policy								
This is the statement of general policy and arrangements for:								
Name of organisation								
Overall and final responsibility for health and safety is that of:								
Name of employer								
Day-to-day responsibility for ensuring this policy is put into practice is delegated to:								

Statement of general policy	Responsibility of *(Name/title)*	Action/arrangements *(Customise to meet your own situation)*
To prevent accidents and cases of work-related ill health and provide adequate control of health and safety risks arising from work activities		
To provide adequate training to ensure employees are competent to do their work		
To engage and consult with employees on day-to-day health and safety conditions and provide advice and supervision on occupational health		
To implement emergency procedures – evacuation in case of fire or other significant incident. You can find help with your fire risk assessment at (*see note 1 below*)		
To maintain safe and healthy working conditions, provide and maintain plant, equipment and machinery, and ensure safe storage/use of substances		
To ensure accidents and incidents are recorded and reported under RIDDOR *(see note 2 below)*		
Health and safety law poster is displayed		
First-aid box and accident book are located		

Subject to review, monitoring and revision by				**Every**		months or sooner if work activity changes	
Name		**Position**		**Signature**		**Date**	

Note 1: *http://www.communities.gov.uk/fire/firesafety/firesafetylaw/*
Note 2: *www.hse.gov.uk/riddor*

GA02 Health, safety and environment risk assessment

Company name			
Project title		Risk assessment no.	
Contract no.		Location	
Person conducting assessment		Date	
Person supervising work		Date	

Persons exposed *(tick box)*

	Employees		Other workers		Public/visitors		Young persons
	New/expectant mothers				Vulnerable persons		Others

Estimated total number of persons at risk	

Hazards *(What might cause harm?)*	S	H	E		S	H	E
1. Adverse weather conditions				17. Loading/unloading			
2. Cold				18. Materials			
3. Electricity				19. Moving parts of machinery			
4. Excavation				20. Proximity to water			
5. Fire/flammable atmosphere				21. Scaffold			
6. Floor/ground conditions				22. Sharp objects			
7. Flying particles/dust				23. Stairs/steps			
8. Hand or power tool				24. Static equipment/machinery			
9. Hazardous substance				25. Structure			
10. Heat/hot work				26. Temporary works			
11. Lack of experience				27. Vehicle/mobile equipment			
12. Lack of training				28. Working hours/fatigue			
13. Lack of/too much oxygen				29. Workstation design			
14. Access				30. Work at height			
15. Lifting equipment appliances				31. Third parties			
16. Lighting				32. Other			

Comments

Risk factor

Risk quantity	No injury, damage or environment impact	Minor injury, damage or environment impact	Specified injury, damage or environment impact	Fatality, building loss or catastrophic environment impact
Almost no probability	A	A	A	U
A small probability	A	A	U	U
A high probability	A	U	U	U
Almost certain	A	U	U	U
	Acceptable		Unacceptable	

Risk level	Action
Insignificant	No action required and no documentary records need to be kept.
Acceptable	No further preventative action. Consideration shall be given to more cost-effective solutions or improvements that impose no additional cost burden. Monitoring required to ensure that controls in place are properly maintained.
Unacceptable	Work shall not be started or continued until the risk level has been reduced to an acceptable risk level. While the control measures selected shall be cost-effective, legally there is an absolute duty to reduce the risk. This means that if it is not possible to reduce the risk, even with unlimited resources, then the work shall not be started or shall remain prohibited.

Notes

1. *Physical hazards are the nature of issues that may cause harm. Tick box for hazard.*
2. *Preventative/control measures are the actions that will stop it going wrong.*
3. *Control measures are to ensure that residual risks are reduced to a minimum. Where controls fail to reduce the risk to an acceptable level then refer assessment to your line manager.*
4. *If the operations are likely to affect the public or the safe operation of a public infrastructure or transport system, the control measures must reduce the likelihood of significant harm to the level that existed before our work commenced.*
5. *Where young persons or expectant mothers are involved in the activity, ensure that any additional controls are put in place in accordance with local procedures.*
6. *In addition to the above, consideration must be given to other individuals' susceptibility due to pre-existing health conditions (such as a bad back or poor hearing). Additional human factors (such as ergonomics and workplace design) should also be considered.*
7. *Where a hazard is identified that is not listed in the physical hazards list, enter the hazard description followed by 'other' in brackets, for example (Other).*

GA

GA02 Health, safety and environment risk assessment *continued*

Hazard number *(from previous page)*	**Nature of risk** *(What might go wrong?)*	**Risk before controls U/A/ insignificant**	**Control measures** *(How do you stop it going wrong?)*	**Control measures implemented by** *(name)*	**Risk after controls U/A/ insignificant**

GA02 Health, safety and environment risk assessment *continued*

Hazard number *(from previous page)*	**Nature of risk** *(What might go wrong?)*	**Risk before controls U/A/ insignificant**	**Control measures** *(How do you stop it going wrong?)*	**Control measures implemented by** *(name)*	**Risk after controls U/A/ insignificant**

Method statement required?		Yes		No	**Method statement number**	

Additional risk assessment *(tick box)*								**PPE** *(tick box)*							
	Noise		COSHH		Handling		New/expectant mothers		Helmet		Respiratory		Boots		Hi-vis
	Asbestos		Lead		Radiation		Young persons		Hearing		Eye		Harness		Others

	Name	**Position**	**Signature**	**Date**
Person completing the assessment				
Person reviewing the assessment				
Date to be reviewed				

This risk assessment must be communicated to operatives before work commences. A separate briefing sheet (GA11) should be used and be made available to the operatives for reference.

GA

GA03 Risk assessment

Company name							
Location				**Project title**			
Risk assessment no.		**Review date**			**Revision no.**		
Person supervising work				**Employer**			
Persons exposed *(tick box)*		**Employees**		**Other workers**		**Public/visitors**	
		Young persons		**Estimated total number of persons at risk**			
		New/expectant mothers		**Vulnerable persons**		**Others**	

Severity					
5	5	10	15	20	25
4	4	8	12	16	20
3	3	6	9	12	15
2	2	4	6	8	10
1	1	2	3	4	5
	1	2	3	4	5

Likelihood

Risk = Likelihood x Severity

Likelihood

Rating 1 = Very unlikely
Rating 2 = Unlikely
Rating 3 = Likely
Rating 4 = Very likely
Rating 5 = Almost certain

Severity

Rating 1 = No injury
Rating 2 = Minor injury or illness
Rating 3 = 7-day injury or illness
Rating 4 = Specified injury or illness
Rating 5 = Fatality, disabling injury, and so on

Acceptable — Further review — Unacceptable

	1	2	3	4	5	6	7	8	9	
Hazard	**Factors of harm**		**Risk** *(Likelihood x Severity)*	**Control measures**	**Factors of harm**		**Residual risk** *(Likelihood x Severity)*	**Control measures implemented by** *(name)*	**Acceptable risk**	
	Likelihood *(1-5)*	**Severity** *(1-5)*			**Likelihood** *(1-5)*	**Severity** *(1-5)*			**Yes**	**No**

GA03 Risk assessment *continued*

Hazard	1	2	3	4	5	6	7	8	9	
	Factors of harm		Risk *(Likelihood x Severity)*	Control measures	Factors of harm		Residual risk *(Likelihood x Severity)*	Control measures implemented by *(name)*	Acceptable risk	
	Likelihood *(1-5)*	Severity *(1-5)*			Likelihood *(1-5)*	Severity *(1-5)*			Yes	No

Persons conducting assessment	Name	Position	Signature	Date

This risk assessment must be communicated to operatives before work commences. A separate briefing sheet (GA11) should be used and be made available to the operatives for reference.

GA

GA

GA04 Return to work risk assessment

Company name		**Project title**	
Location		**Contract no.**	
Name of person returning to work		**Date of birth**	
Occupation		**Period of absence from work**	

Nature of injury, illness or condition that rendered the person unfit for work	**Department/site**

Has a fit note been obtained from the doctor?		Yes		No
Is occupational health advice required? If 'Yes' state advice given.		Yes		No

Proposed working hours *(using 24-hour clock)*	**Safety induction carried out by**
Nature of work to be undertaken	**Specific work that must not be undertaken**
Specific hazards/risk identified	**Control measures required**
Agreed risk assessment review date	

Risk assessment prepared and brief by							
Name		**Position**		**Signature**		**Date**	
I have been briefed on this risk assessment							
Name		**Position**		**Signature**		**Date**	

Note: *the health and safety briefing must include the:*

- *risks identified by the assessment*
- *preventative/protective measures required to ensure the employee's health and safety*
- *duties/tasks that are forbidden*
- *emergency procedures and how they will be implemented*
- *first-aid arrangements.*

GA05 Expectant mothers' risk assessment

Company name		**Project title**	
Location		**Contract no.**	
Name of expectant mother		**Employee number**	
Occupation		**Department**	
Line manager		**Date of notification**	

Brief details of activities involved in performing job role	**Specific work that must not be undertaken**

List of agents/working conditions	**What is the risk?**	**How to avoid the risk**	**Legislation**
Physical agents			
Chemical agents			
Biological agents			
Other working conditions			

Control measures to be employed, emergency procedures and first aid/welfare arrangements

Any additional training requirements

Proposed/agreed working hours *(using 24-hour clock)*	**The expectant mother shall be supervised by**
Agreed risk assessment review date	

Risk assessment prepared and briefed by							
Name		**Position**		**Signature**		**Date**	
I have been briefed on this risk assessment							
Name		**Position**		**Signature**		**Date**	

Note: *the health and safety briefing must include the:*

- *risks identified by the assessment*
- *preventative/protective measures required to ensure the employee's health and safety*
- *duties/tasks that are forbidden*
- *emergency procedures and how they will be implemented*
- *first-aid arrangements.*

GA

GA06 Young persons' risk assessment

Company name		**Project title**	
Location		**Contract no.**	
Name of young person		**Date of birth**	

Date of employment/work experience commenced	**Department/site**
Proposed/agreed working hours *(using 24-hour clock)*	**Young person supervised by**
	Safety induction carried out by
Nature of work to be undertaken	**Specific work that must not be undertaken**
Specific hazards/risk identified	**Control measures required**
Specific training required by the young person	
Agreed risk assessment review date	

Risk assessment prepared and briefed by							
Name		**Position**		**Signature**		**Date**	
I have been briefed on this risk assessment							
Name		**Position**		**Signature**		**Date**	

Note: *the briefing shall include the:*

- *the risks identified by the assessment*
- *the preventative/protective/control measures required, ensuring the young person's health and safety*
- *the emergency procedures and how they will be implemented*
- *the first aid/welfare arrangements*
- *a warning against horseplay.*

GA07 Post-completion defect work risk assessment

Company name				**Project title**			
Location				**Contract no.**			
Address							
Reason for assessment		**Six month defects**		**12 month defects**		**Other** *(state)*	
Sub-contractor(s)							
Brief description of work/defects/ call out							

Have details of defects/reason for call out been passed onto those carrying out the work?		Yes		No
Is work to be carried out in live/occupied premises?		Yes		No
If 'Yes' are there any client requirements, access restrictions or site rules (*state below*)?				

Tick PPE required										**Other** *(state)*	

Will work require lone working?		Yes		No
If 'Yes' state precautions/checks *(raising alarm, first aid, etc.)* (*state below*)				
Is work deemed high risk?		Yes		No
If 'Yes' a separate risk assessment is required	Risk assessment no.			
If 'No' state control measures required, including task PPE, access, manual handling, COSHH, and so on (*state below*)				

What working at height/access is required? (*tick below*)			
	Existing (such as 'safe' type system)	⚠	**Must be trained in the use of, prior to starting work.**
	Scissor lift/cherry picker/MEWP	⚠	**Must be trained** operator (e.g. IPAF) plus risk assessment.
	Mobile tower	⚠	**Must be trained** to erect and use (e.g. PASMA).
	Podium steps/room mate	⚠	**Erect correctly, lock wheels** – no over reaching.
	Stepladder	⚠	Short duration work only **plus complete ladder permit.**
	Ladder	⚠	**Access only – else complete ladder permit.**
	Other	⚠	Include any training or special requirements.

State plant, equipment and materials *(including disposal measures)* to be used
State any other issues/comments

Assessment completed by							
Name		**Position**		**Signature**		**Date**	
The works have been completed, as detailed above, and the area left safe and clean							
Name		**Position**		**Signature**		**Date**	

This risk assessment must be communicated to operatives before work commences. A separate briefing sheet *(refer to GA11)* should be used and be made available to operatives for reference.

GA

GA08 Method statement

Company name		**Project title**	
Location		**Contract no.**	
Method statement title		**Reference**	
Description of work			

This method statement has been developed and must be read with the following risk assessments	
Risk assessment reference	**Title**
Work commences on	
Areas to be worked in	
Duration of work *(actual or estimated)*	
Number of workers *(actual or estimated)*	

Personnel *(include details of all personnel involved in the task and any specific training, skills or qualifications required)*		
Name	**Position**	**Competence details**

Emergency arrangement details			
Fire/evacuation	First aid	Emergency spill kit Pollution/spill	Other

Personal protective equipment (PPE) requirements								
							Other	Other
Head (EN 397)	Foot (BS EN 345-1)	Hi-vis vest	Hand (BS EN 388)	Eye (EN166)	Hearing (EN 352-1)	Fall arrest		

Construction dust (***Note:*** *construction dust is harmful and can lead to fatal lung diseases such as silicosis)*				
Will the work create dust or fumes?		Yes		No
Identify specific control measures to avoid or minimise dust or fumes				
Identify respiratory protective equipment (RPE) that will be required if dust or fumes cannot be avoided				

GA08 Method statement *continued*

Hazardous materials								
Are hazardous materials to be used?		Yes		No	Are COSHH/DSEAR data sheets available?		Yes		No
Attach or identify specific controls required from COSHH risk assessment								

Permit required *(tick below)*					
	Permit to work *(general)*		Permit to enter *(confined spaces)*		Permit to dig
	Hot-work permit		Out of hours work permit		Other
Details of person issuing permit					

Description of safe method of work

(Where appropriate include information such as sketches, details of significant risk control, sequence of works, etc.)

Tools, plant and equipment	
Type	**Details of inspections/test certificates**

Briefing register

A copy of this briefing register must be attached to the method statement, together with other relevant information *(such as the associated risk assessments, permits or COSHH assessments)*.

GA

GA08 Method statement *continued*

Supervisor in charge of the work							
I confirm that I have read and understand the requirements of this method statement and associated risk assessments and have communicated them to operatives under my control and to those who may be affected by its requirements. ***Note:*** *it is important that you test the operatives' understanding and assume they have read and understood the method statement and risk assessments.*							
Name		**Position**		**Signature**		**Date**	

Operatives/workforce carrying out the work			
I understand and will agree to adhere to the contents of this method statement and the associated risk assessments. I have attended a site induction/briefing that explained the general site rules and necessary site specific arrangements.			
Name	**Position**	**Signature**	**Date**

If you have any doubt about information given or contained in this method statement – ask for clarification.

GA09 Method statement review

Method statement – content review and tracking sheet

Company name		**Project title**	
Location		**Contract no.**	
Method statement title			
Date issued to site management			
Proposed date of work to start on site			

Project/site manager	**1st review date**	**Status***	**Name**	**2nd review date**	**Status***	**Name**
Temporary works co-ordinator (as required)	**1st review date**	**Status***	**Name**	**2nd review date**	**Status***	**Name**
Technical advisor (as required)	**1st review date**	**Status***	**Name**	**2nd review date**	**Status***	**Name**
H,S&E function (as required)	**1st review date**	**Status***	**Name**	**2nd review date**	**Status***	**Name**

(Method statement content is to be reviewed in accordance with the prompt list overleaf).

Comments/observations *(if appropriate)*

**** Status user notes***

Complete 1st review using prompt list overleaf. Once complete, make an assessment on status (see below). If status is A then no further action is required. If B or C, return the method statement with the prompt list and comments/observations. Re-assess amended method statement (2nd review) following the same process until status A is achieved.

Status:
- *A – Work can proceed as described*
- *B – Work can proceed when comments are incorporated*
- *C – Re-submit and review before work can proceed*

Signed off by activity supervisor

Name		**Position**		**Signature**		**Date**	

Signed off by site management as current working document

Name		**Position**		**Signature**		**Date**	

Note: *clearance to proceed with this method statement does not relieve the sub-contractor of their contractual obligations, including safety, structural integrity or any implications to permanent works arising from these proposals.*

GA09 Method statement review *continued*

Method statement review – prompt list

Note: *this list could also be used when preparing method statements.*

Method statement review – prompt list				
1. Description	**Yes**	**No**	**In part**	**N/A**
Fully describes the work, tasks, sequence, method and process for change?				
Programme of works and working hours identified?				
2. Resources	**Yes**	**No**	**In part**	**N/A**
Names and titles of key personnel/supervisors responsible?				
Details of resources required (such as equipment, plant, workers and materials)?				
Certificates of competence or qualification of operatives provided?				
Certificates for plant/equipment inspection/examination provided?				
Crane/lifting equipment – certificates/checklist/lifting plan in place?				
Sub-contracted work element/personnel.				
3. Hazard identification	**Yes**	**No**	**In part**	**N/A**
Specific risk assessment attached and satisfactory? Have all the risks been evaluated?				
Are there arrangements in place for reviewing control measures due to changing circumstances?				
Approval of sub-contractor's risk assessment and method statement?				
Access/scaffolding (including ancillary arrangements, such as anchor points) fully detailed and described?				
COSHH, noise and manual handling issues dealt with?				
Workplace environment, design, layout, limitations identified and human factors taken into consideration (such as experience, fatigue, and so on)?				
4. Control measures	**Yes**	**No**	**In part**	**N/A**
Supervision?				
High risk or safety critical work identified and controls specified?				
Permit requirements identified?				
Monitoring (checks and inspections) identified?				
Environmental controls/waste disposal identified?				
Details of toolbox talks to be provided?				
Personal protective equipment specified?				
5. Emergency arrangement	**Yes**	**No**	**In part**	**N/A**
Rescue – how – by whom?				
First aid requirements?				
Spillage containment?				
Special welfare?				
6. Temporary works	**Yes**	**No**	**In part**	**N/A**
Details of temporary works schemes identified, including all documents?				
Temporary protection/support identified (such as fire, traffic and services)?				

GA09 Method statement review *continued*

Method statement review – prompt list

7. Interfaces	Yes	No	In part	N/A
Interfaces/security of the client/public/other contractors identified?				
Any builder's work in connection identified/adequate notice given?				
Security?				
Traffic routes, emergency arrangements, services and existing method statements?				
8. Training and information	**Yes**	**No**	**In part**	**N/A**
Conformation of briefing of method statement to operatives?				
Special training (confined space, tower erection, use of plant, and so on)?				
9. Environmental issues	**Yes**	**No**	**In part**	**N/A**
Environmental risks?				
Statutory permit and licence conditions?				
Pollution prevention?				
10. Monitoring and compliance	**Yes**	**No**	**In part**	**N/A**
Monitoring – by whom?				
Enforcement – how – by whom – equipment, sampling?				
Testing and commissioning?				
Checking, review and update?				
Change requirements?				
Confirmation of operative's briefing?				
Any other (specify)?				

Comments

Name		Position		Signature		Date	

GA

GA10 Risk assessment and method statement review

Company name		**Project title**	
Location		**Contract no.**	
Risk assessment and method statement for activity			
Preparing company		**Prepared by**	
Document reference no. (if any)		**Revision**	

Record of principal contractor's review. (Results of review to be formally communicated to preparing company.)

Check	Guidance on aspects that should be covered	Adequate? *(See comments)* Yes	No
1. Scope of work	Brief description of work with scope defined by area, floor or structure (where specified conditions dictate). Should also define any limitations of use and **must be site specific**.		
2. Organisation	Key staff involved in managing and supervising the work and the anticipated type of labour required, including any required induction, training and proof of competence.		
3. Materials	Materials required, including storage location, any identifying marks and any special safety measures to be taken during storage, handling, use and protection. COSHH details as required.		
4. Plant/equipment	Major plant and equipment required, including any lifting equipment and any plant or equipment calibration/certification/12-monthly or 6-monthly for chains/ weekly inspections.		
5. Preparation	Details of any permit approvals, notices or completion of other work needed prior to starting work (such as permit to dig, work or load), electrical isolations, mechanical isolations, commissioning, access proposals, restrictions and requirements.		
6. Safety and health	Safety and health of all who may be affected (employees/third parties), including anticipated hazards and required precautions (included or by reference to risk assessment). PPE, access, egress, control of work at height, husbandry, first aider, barriers, training, planning, inspections, communication, etc.		
7. Environment	Anticipated hazards or special conditions requiring precautions (such as traffic conditions, waste management/disposal, dust or noise, ground conditions, watercourses, environmentally sensitive areas and wildlife protected) and appropriate mitigation measures.		
8. Emergency procedures	Procedures and arrangements for dealing with health, safety or environmental incidents and accidents (overarching is company/site management incident investigation process).		
9. Method and sequence	Definition of how the work is to be carried out, including the proposed sequence and any temporary works. (Required for complex operations only.)		
10. Protection	Protection of partly and fully completed work against damage, deterioration, third parties and/or the public.		
11. Inspections/ checks/tests	Required prior to, during and on completion of work. Any hold points where approval to continue is required and who can release them.		
12. Records	To be obtained or produced during and on completion of the work.		
This document is/is not* considered suitable and sufficient to allow the work outlined above to commence.			
All site supervisors and operatives undertaking the activity must be aware of and understand the risk assessment and method statement. It is important that the risks and controls are explained and understanding tested.			

(Delete as applicable.)*

GA10 Risk assessment and method statement review *continued*

Comments	
1.	
2.	
3.	
4.	
5.	
6.	
7.	
8.	
9.	
10.	
11.	
12.	

Name		Position		Signature		Date	

GA11 Briefing sheet

Company name		**Project title**	
Location		**Contract no.**	

Briefing for *(tick below)*

	Risk assessment		Method statement		Toolbox talk
	Pre-task briefing		Permit briefing		Worker engagement
	Other *(state)*				

Activity/subject	
Project/location	

List of persons attending briefing *(obtain signatures at end of briefing as a record of attendance)*.

Name	Trade	Company	Signature

Workforce feedback and comments

Briefing delivered by

Name		**Position**		**Signature**		**Date**	

GA

GA12 Induction training checklist

Company name		Project title	
Location		Contract no.	

	Access		Electricity		Liquefied petroleum gas		Safety signs and notices
	Accident reporting		Emergency evacuation		Manual handling		Scaffolding (incl. mobile scaffolds)
	Alcohol and drugs		Emergency procedure		Medication		Site layout
	Asbestos		Environment		Method statements		Site security
	Assembly points		Escape routes		Mobile elevating work platforms		Skin protection
	Boundaries		Excavations		Near-miss incidents		Smoking
	CDM Regulations		Eye protection		Needles and syringes		Tidiness (housekeeping)
	Competence		Fall arrest		Noise		Toilets
	Confidential issues		Fall prevention		Occupational health		Traffic routes
	Confined spaces		Fire		Overhead electricity cables		Training
	Consultation with employees		First aid		Permits to work		Types of injury
	Contamination		Flammable liquids		Personal protective equipment		Underground services
	COSHH		Health and safety committee		Plant and equipment		Vehicles and deliveries
	CSCS cards		Hearing protection zones		Powers of inspectors		Vibration
	Dangerous occurrences		High-visibility clothing		Registration schemes		Waste disposal
	Dermatitis		Hoists		Reporting defects		Waste minimisation
	Discipline		Ladders/stepladders		Restricted or prohibited areas		Welfare facilities
	Dress code		Lasers		Risk assessments		Working at height
	Drying rooms		Legal issues		Safe systems of work		Working near, on or over water
	Dust and fumes		Lifting equipment		Safety harnesses		
	Edge protection		Lighting		Safety policy		

Comments

Name		Position		Signature		Date	

GA

GA13 Site induction register

Company name		Project title	
Location		Contract no.	

I confirm that I have attended the site induction, understand the site rules and that I am not taking medication or drugs that could affect my concentration or safety on site.

Ref no.	Date	Name *(capitals)*	Signature*	Employed by	Occupation	Approved competency card/ certificate held *(i.e. CSCS/CPCS)*		Type of card held *(plus any relevant categories and card number)*	Person giving induction
						Yes	No		

GA14 Human factors checklist

The checklist below has been taken from the Health and Safety Executive's Human factors Briefing Note 1.

This list doesn't cover every aspect of human factors but will give you an idea of what is involved. It includes safety management factors. If you can tick most of the boxes then your company is probably dealing with human factors and safety culture issues quite well, but every company can improve.

Company name		**Project title**	
Location		**Contract no.**	

Health and Safety Executive *Human factors checklist*		
For all the jobs done on this site, this company usually	**Yes**	**No**
1. Chooses the most skilled people to do the work, either our own people or contractors.		
2. Gives people interesting and varied work without overloading them.		
3. Arranges for work to be done in teams if that's the best approach.		
4. Takes care that the working environment is not too hot or cold or uncomfortable.		
5. Keeps noise levels down to help communications and concentration.		
6. Provides good lighting.		
7. Arranges reasonable working hours, meal and rest breaks.		
8. Makes sure that there's enough room to work in; that is, not too cramped or confined.		
9. Issues written instructions and other essential paperwork that work very well.		
10. Avoids overloading people with information and doesn't give contradictory information.		
11. Provides the proper tools and equipment to do the work.		
12. Doesn't apply unreasonable time pressure.		
13. Minimises interruptions to jobs and doesn't change priorities all the time.		
14. Makes sure that, if a job is handed over to another shift, important information is handed over with it.		
15. Provides good supervision of important tasks or of less experienced teams.		
16. Has practised and realistic emergency plans in place in case there's a problem.		
17. Encourages a good working culture and good relationships between people.		
18. Doesn't keep changing the organisation, individual responsibilities or lines of management.		
Comments		

Name		**Position**		**Signature**		**Date**	

GA

GA15 Health, safety and environment inspection report

Company name		**Project title**			
Location		**Contract no.**			
Supervisor/manager		**Sheet**		**of**	
Key	N = No action	Y = Action required	**blank** = Not seen or applicable		

1.		Access equipment	**2.**		Accidents/near misses	**3.**		Asbestos
4.		Community engagement	**5.**		Competence/training	**6.**		Consents/permits, etc.
7.		Construction phase plan	**8.**		Consultation/toolbox talks	**9.**		COSHH
10.		Demolition	**11.**		Dust and fumes	**12.**		Ecology
13.		Edge protection/barriers	**14.**		Energy/resource use	**15.**		Excavations/earthworks
16.		Fire and first aid	**17.**		Hand-held tools/equipment	**18.**		Health risks
19.		HFL/fuel storage	**20.**		Housekeeping	**21.**		Inductions
22.		Ladders/steps/podiums	**23.**		Lifting operations	**24.**		Lighting/temp electrics
25.		Live services	**26.**		Manual handling	**27.**		Material delivery/storage
28.		Method statements	**29.**		MEWPs, etc.	**30.**		Mobile plant
31.		Noise and vibration	**32.**		Notices and signage	**33.**		Occupational health
34.		Other	**35.**		Permits	**36.**		Pollution prevention
37.		PPE	**38.**		Previous report closed out	**39.**		Registers and records
40.		Respiratory risks	**41.**		Risk assessments	**42.**		Safe access/egress
43.		Scaffolding	**44.**		Security/public protection	**45.**		Site establishment
46.		Temporary works	**47.**		Traffic management	**48.**		Vehicle unloading
49.		Waste management	**50.**		Welfare facilities	**51.**		Work at height

Item no.	**Areas for improvement/advice/positive observations**	**Action by**	**Action date**

Person completing inspection							
Name		**Position**		**Signature**		**Date**	
Report received by							
Name		**Position**		**Signature**		**Date**	

GA15 Health, safety and environment inspection report *continued*

Company name		Project title			
Location		Contract no.			
Supervisor/manager		Sheet		of	

Item no.	Areas for improvement/advice/positive observations	Action by	Action date

Comments							
Person completing inspection							
Name		Position		Signature		Date	
Report received by							
Name		Position		Signature		Date	

GA16 Near miss or learning event report (Part 1)

To be completed and handed to site management

Company name		**Project title**	
Location		**Contract no.**	
Name			
Date		**Time**	
Classification *(tick)*			

	Health		**Safety**		**Environment**

Details of the learning event *(include all relevant information)*

Please report anything that is unsafe or a near miss

Unsafe conditions

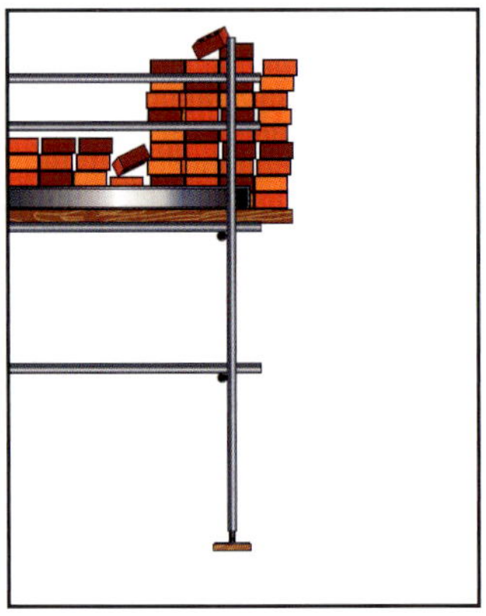

Something with the potential to cause harm

Near misses

An incident that nearly resulted in an injury or damage

Accidents

An incident that resulted in an injury or damage

It really does help to prevent accidents

Name		**Position**		**Signature**		**Date**	

GA17 Near miss or learning event report (Part 2)

GA

To be completed by site management

Company name			
Project title		**Contract no.**	
Date		**Location**	
Reported by		**Part 1 – date received**	

Classification *(tick)*					
	Health		**Safety**		**Environment**
	Main contractor		**Sub-contractor**		**Third party/public**

Details of the learning event *(include all relevant information)*

Potential outcome *(tick)*		**Potential severity** *(tick)*	
	Personal injury		Negligible
	Property or equipment damage		Slight
	Environmental issue		Moderate
	Other *(state)*		High
			Very high

Lessons learned (consider immediate and root causes) *(tick)*			
Work environment			
	Defective workplace		Design/layout
	Housekeeping		Lack of room
	Lighting		Noise/distraction
	Weather		Access/egress
Management			
	System of work		Supervision
	Training		Communication
	Management of change		
Plant/equipment			
	Construction/design		Installation
	Safety device		Operation/use
	Mechanical failure		Maintenance

GA

GA17 Near miss or learning event report (Part 2) *continued*

Human factors			
	Failure to follow rules		Instructions misunderstood
	Error of judgement		Lack of experience
	Unsafe attitude		Undue haste
	Horseplay		Lapse of concentration
	Fatigue		Working without authorisation
PPE			
	Design		Wrong type used
	Maintenance		Not provided/unavailable
	Not used		
Other			
	Third party		Under investigation
	Other *(state)*		

Follow up

Actions required	Responsible	Completed

Name		Position		Signature		Date	

GA18 Weekly project SHE inspection

Company name		**Project title**	
Location		**Contract no.**	

A	**Site activities being inspected**	**Date**		**Time (24 hrs)**	
Activity		**Employee or contractor(s)**			

Item no.	Element, checks and records		Office (O) /Site (S)	Yes	NC*	NA**
CO1	Corporate image/ information	Compound set up, signage, cleanliness, staff dress, attitude, SHE awards, policies, EL insurance, first aiders, etc.	S & O			
RA1	Risk assessment	Copy available at site (specific to activity and authorised)	S			
RA2		Controls identified in place and complied with: risk assessment and method statement review sheet completed	S			
RA4		Evidence of communication – operatives signed into risk assessment	O			
MS1	Method statement	Copy available at site (specific to activity and authorised)	S			
MS2		Controls identified in place and complied with	S			
MS3		Evidence of communication – operatives signed into method statement	O			
WH1	Work at height	Prevention of falls from height or falling materials and are they adequate (e.g. work platforms with suitable edge protection or safety harnesses)? Are services trenches protected, fragile roof, statutory inspections, scaff tags, podiums, stepladders, hop ups?	S			
WH2		Ladders and podium platforms are in good order and free from defects	O			
L1	Lifting	If lifting operations are in progress, asset tags are legible and intact, checked and valid for cranes, hiabs, telehandlers, excavators, etc.	S			
N1	Noise	If noisy operations are in progress is hearing protection being worn and has an assessment been made? Are measures in place to prevent activities creating a statutory nuisance in terms of noise?	S			
V1	Vibration	If using equipment that is causing hand-arm vibration are staff aware of and complying with trigger times?	S			
V2		Are measures in place to prevent activities creating a statutory nuisance in terms of vibration (e.g. traffic flow near properties)?	S			
MH1	Manual handling	If operatives are lifting heavy items is a manual handling assessment in place – part of activity risk assessment?	S			
PT	Permit systems	Hot works, confined space, permit to dig, permit to load, etc.	S & O			

Waste/environment

E1	Waste (if materials are being taken off site obtain carriers name and destination of load)	Material type				
		Carriers details				
		Name of tip				
E2		Check waste transfer note is in place	O			
E3		Register carrier's licence on file	O			
E4	Environmental issues	Copy of tip/transfer station licence available	O			
E5		Right waste being put in right skip and labelled skips	S			
E6	Pollution prevention guidance	Site registered as a hazardous waste producer	O			
E7		Consignments notes in place for hazardous waste uniquely numbered (rule of 3- producer-carrier-receiver)	O			
E8		In relation to the selected activity are the necessary permissions/ licenses/consents in place (e.g. discharge from interceptors)?	S			
E9		Oil/diesel storage are in bunds and no evidence of significant spillages, spill kits, emergency response	S			
E10		Exemption for recycled materials from the EA (e.g. 19A, WRAP)	O			
E11		Wildlife (tree or ground nesting birds, bats, badger, licences, etc.)	O & S			
E12		Public/private nuisance (dust, noise, lighting, etc.)	O & S			

* *Not checked*
** *Not applicable*

GA

GA18 Weekly project SHE inspection *continued*

Item no.	Element, checks and records	Office (O) /Site (S)	Yes	NC*	NA**
	Workplace				
W1	Access/egress – suitable and safe, planned, maintained	S			
W2	Site security (compound/site/adequately fenced/trespassers)	S			
W3	Housekeeping (site tidy and to an acceptable standard – slips, trips and falls)	S			
W4	Dust/mud suppression (is dust or mud a problem and is it being adequately controlled, cutting works using dust suppression)	S			
W5	Site traffic management (signs, parking, fences, traffic plan)	S & O			
W7	Lighting (adequate for operations in place, including task lighting)	S			
W8	Welfare is clean and tidy and cooking facilities are clean, adequate for numbers	S			
W9	Pedestrian routes (are pedestrians adequately provided for/suitable public protection?)	S			
W10	Temporary works (inspected, designed, temporary work co-ordinator, roof protection, falsework, formwork)	S & O			
W11	Excavation (fenced, design, PTD, signage)	S			
P	**People – Workforce**				
	Name of person(s) selected to review training/risk assessments/induction records *(state below)*				
P1	PPE correct (mandatory and those identified by risk assessment)	S			
P2	Evidence of induction – check register at office	O			
P3	Evidence of training (for example, **CPCS, LANTRA, NPL, IPAF, NASWRA**, etc.)	O			
P4	Evidence of last toolbox talk and risk assessment briefings	S & O			
P5	Behavioural (attitude, knowledge of task, tidiness, equipment, dress, etc.)	S			
PE	**Plant and equipment (including fixed installations)**				
PE1	Tool/equipment (weekly inspections being carried out by the operator/users)	S			
PE2	Is statutory inspection fixed installation (for example, compressors, mechanical, electrical, asbestos, gas, etc.)	O			
PE4	Drip trays in place when carrying out filter duties (oil and diesel)	S			
PE5	Availability and location of emergency spill kit	S			
PE6	Refuelling operations controlled	S			
	Lifting equipment *(select one, if being used note type and serial numbers)*				
	Details of equipment				
	Serial numbers				
PE7	Are thorough (e.g. 12 and six monthly) examination certifications on file and in date?	O			
PE8	General condition of lifting equipment (check for damage, incorrect use, etc.)	S			
PE9	Has it been PAT tested in last three months (check for sticker or tag)?	S			
PE10	General condition (cables, transformers, spider boxes, hand tools, etc.)	S			
PE11	Are daily plant operator sheets being completed and, where defects are noted, repairs done?	S & O			
M	**Materials**				
M1	Storage of materials (safe, prevent loss, damage or contamination, collapse)	S			
M2	COSHH – if hazardous, is COSHH assessment available, briefed to workforce?	S			
M3	COSHH – are controls detailed in assessment being complied with?	S			

* *Not checked*
** *Not applicable*

GA18 Weekly project SHE inspection *continued*

Item no.	Element, checks and records	Office (O) /Site (S)	Yes	NC*	NA**
V	**VDU users**				
V1	Enough room for each person (11 m^2)	S			
V2	Desk free from glare, blinds available, artificial lighting (diffuser)	S			
V3	Self-assessment been carried out by habitual users	S			
V4	VDU users are free from flicker or glare, ergonomic principles been applied, noise, dust, etc.	S			
WE	**Welfare**				
WE1	Are there sufficient facilities for the people in the area?	S			
WE2	Is lighting, heating and ventilation adequate in all facilities?	S			
WE3	Have facilities been cleaned and waste removed?	S			
WE4	Are drinking water and cups available?	S			
WE5	Is hot/warm water, soap, towel/dryer available?	S			
WE6	Has appropriate information been posted (e.g. first aiders, route to hospital, emergency contact details, and site rules, posters, policies, etc.)?	S			
FI	**Fire**				
FI1	Fire risk assessment and fire-fighting equipment suitable, sufficient and tested	S			
FI2	Fire escape (fire escape routes, disabled person(s) obstructions, lighting, etc.)	S & O			
FI3	Assessment(s) (newly installed materials, petrol, solvents, cylinders, etc.)	S			
FI4	Fire prevention (permit systems, debris removal, electrical and test, smoking, etc.)	S			

Weekly SHE inspection action sheet

To be completed by sampler			To be completed by person responsible	
Item	**Problem observed/comments**	**Person responsible**	**Corrective action taken**	**Actioned** *(initial and date)*

Person completing inspection							
Name		**Position**		**Signature**		**Date**	
Received by site management							
Name		**Position**		**Signature**		**Date**	

* Not checked
** Not applicable

GA

GA19 Accident/incident report

Instructions for use

1. To be completed and returned as soon as possible after any incident/accident *(please **print** clearly).*
2. To be used for all incidents (minor and reportable), dangerous occurrences, near misses, environmental incidents, complaints, thefts and incidents involving material damage, including cable strikes.
3. Keep site copy in a secure place (Data Protection Act).

Company name			**This form consists of**		**pages**
Incident date		**Incident time** *(24-hour clock)*			

Incident type *(tick boxes for all that apply and then complete further parts of this form as indicated)*

	Fatality*	**Parts A, B (i and ii) and F**		Minor incident/injury (no first aid)	**Parts A, B (i and ii) and F**
	Specified injury*	**Parts A, B (i and ii) and F**		Dangerous occurrence* (RIDDOR reportable)	**Parts A ,B (ii) and F**
	Over seven-day injury*	**Parts A, B (i and ii) and F**		Environmental incident	**Parts A, C and F**
	Reportable disease*	**Parts A, B (i and ii) and F**		Near miss/dangerous occurrence (Not RIDDOR reportable)	**Parts A and F**
	Ill health	**Parts A, B (i and ii) and F**		Utility damage	**Parts A, D and F**
	First aid (on site)	**Parts A, B (i and ii) and F**		Theft/vandalism/violence	**Parts A, E and F (also B (i) for violence)**
	Medical treatment (off site)	**Parts A, B (i and ii) and F**		Complaint	**Parts A and F**
*HSE incident notification number			**Date reported**		

Part A – Description of incident

Where on site did the incident occur?									
Were photographs taken?		Yes		No	*(please include a copy with this form)*	**Were samples taken?**		Yes		No

Describe what happened and how. *In the case of an injury, state what the injured person was doing at the time and side of body (left or right). (Where possible, take photographs of the general area but not of injured persons.) In the case of an environmental incident, state the events that caused the incident (details of plant involved, photographs, wherever practicable, must be taken). In the case of damage, indicate if damage is to permanent works, temporary works, plant, temporary buildings/contents, employees permanent effects. (Photographs must be taken.)*

Please sketch the general area of the incident *(include any relevant measurements)*
(If more space is required, please attach additional sheets and include references to them in this box)

Name		**Position**		**Employer**			
Can it be established what company caused the incident?				Yes		No	N/A

Give details *(company's name and individual's name)*

GA19 Accident/incident report *continued*

GA

Part B – Health and safety

Part B(i) – Details of injured person

Surname		**Forename(s)**		**Date of birth**		**Signature** *(if possible)*	
Address							
Postcode		**Contact telephone no.**		**Position**			

Was any time lost?		Yes		No	**Date work finished**		**Time work finished**		**Date work restarted**		**Time work restarted**

Name and telephone no. of hospital *(where applicable)*	
Detail all PPE required by the risk assessment for the operation	
Detail all PPE worn at time of incident	
Details of person's employer *(name, address and telephone).* **If member of the public then write 'public'**	

Location of injury *(tick boxes for all that apply)*

	Head		Chest		Arm/shoulder		Finger		Foot		Other *(state below)*
	Face/neck		Abdomen		Wrist		Leg/hip		Respiratory system	
	Eye		Back		Hand		Ankle		Digestive system	

Type of injury *(tick boxes for all that apply)*

	Amputation		Strain/sprain		Foreign body		Multiple		Crush
	Bruising/swelling		Asphyxiation/gassing		Fracture		Shock/concussion		Ingestion
	Dislocation		Loss of consciousness		Burn/scald		Puncture		Internal
	Electric shock		Cut/laceration/abrasion		Whiplash		Ill health		Other *(state below)*

Was the injured person advised to see their doctor or visit a hospital?						Yes		No	
Is drug or alcohol testing required?		Yes		No	**Details of result**		Positive		Negative

Part B(ii) – Details of incident

Basic cause of incident *(tick one box only)*

	Fall from height		Manual handling		Repetitive motion/action
	Fall on same level		Contact with tool/equipment/machinery		Collision
	Fall down stairs/steps		Contact with flying particle		Fire
	Struck by moving object		Contact with electricity		Explosion
	Struck by falling object		Contact with/exposed to heat/acid		Drowning
	Struck/trapped by something collapsed/overturning		Contact with/exposed to air/water pressure		Loss of containment/unintentional release
	Trapped between objects		Contact with/exposed to hazardous substance		Asphyxiation
	Step on/struck against stationary object		Exposure to noise/vibration		Other *(state)*

Source of hazard *(tick one box only)*

	Lifting equipment		Scaffold		Temporary works		Flying particle
	Vehicle/mobile equipment		Excavation		Materials		Dust
	Static equipment/machinery		Stairs/steps		Floor/ground condition		Proximity to water
	Moving parts of machinery		Working surface		Lack of oxygen		Workstation layout
	Power tool		Structure		Heat/hot work		Hazardous substance
	Hand tool		Ladder		Cold		Other *(state)*

GA19 Accident/incident report *continued*

Part C – Environmental incident

Type of incident *(tick boxes for all that apply)*

	Air pollution		Noise or vibration		Plants or wildlife		Fly tipping
	Water contamination		Ground contamination		Waste disposal		Other *(state below)*

Severity of incident *(tick one box only)*

	Minor		Significant		Major

Has incident been reported to the environment agency/NRW/SEPA?		Yes		No	**Contact details/reference**	

Part D – Utility damage

Description of service		**Owner of service**	

Cause of damage *(please tick as appropriate)*

	Mechanical plant		Hand-operated plant		Hand tools
	Other *(state)*				

Plant owner's name/plant hire company's name	
If the plant was on hire, state who to	

Who undertook the repair of the service?		**Date and time repair undertaken**	

Was the service clearly shown on permit to dig?		Yes		No	**If 'No' state why**	

In your opinion, state company responsible for the damage		**Will they be invoiced direct by utility company?**		Yes		No	**If 'No' state why**	

Details of communications with company responsible for damage

Date on correspondence		**Reference of correspondence** *(such as unique letter reference)*	

Part E – Theft/vandalism/violence

List affected items/works involved *(including serial numbers/plant numbers and value if known)*, if applicable

Details of owner *(name and address)*, if applicable

Crime number/police log reference		**Date and time reported**		**Name of person who reported the incident**	

GA19 Accident/incident report *continued*

Part F – Root cause and prevention *(tick boxes for all that apply)*

Work environment							
	Defective workplace		Lighting		Design/layout		Noise/distraction
	Housekeeping		Weather		Lack of room		Access/egress
Human factors							
	Failure to follow rules		Lack of experience		Failure to adhere to risk assessment, and so on		Fatigue
	Instructions misunderstood		Unsafe attitude		Horseplay		Working without authorisation
	Error of judgement		Undue haste		Lapse of concentration		
PPE							
	Design		Maintenance/defective		Not used		
	Wrong type used		Not provided/unavailable				
Management							
	Non-communication of risk		Supervision		Training		System failure
Plant/equipment							
	Construction/design		Safety device		Mechanical failure		
	Installation		Operation/use		Maintenance		
Other							
	Third party		Under investigation		Other *(state)*		

Details of actions taken immediately following the incident to recover the situation

Action taken (or suggested) to prevent reoccurrence and to communicate lessons learnt from the incident

Person completing the form

Name		**Position**		**Signature**		**Date**	

Person with overall workplace responsibility

Name		**Position**		**Signature**		**Date**	

GA

GA20 Accident report

Company name		Project title	
Location		Contract no.	

1. Name of employer							
2. Site address							
		Contact name					
3. Injured person's surname		Forenames					
4. Injured person's address							
5. National Insurance no.		Age		Date of birth			
6. Normal occupation							
7. Occupation at time of accident							
8. Exact location of accident							
9. Date and time of accident		Date		Time			
10. Date and time of ceasing work		Date		Time			
11. Precise nature of injury *(if eye or limb, state left or right)*							
12. To who was the accident reported?							
		Date		Time			
13. HSE or Incident Contact Centre informed by telephone, fax or email							
Telephone / Fax / email		Date		Time			
14. F2508 report sent to the HSE on		Date		Time			
15. Accident recorded in the official company register *(if applicable)*					Yes		No
16. Was first aid given on site? If 'Yes' state name of first aider.					Yes		No
If treatment was received from a doctor, state name							
17. Did the injured person go to hospital?					Yes		No
Give name of hospital							
18. Was the injured person authorised to be at the place of the accident for the purpose of their work?					Yes		No
19. How was the accident caused?							
a) Give a full description of what happened							
b) State what the injured person was doing at the time							
c) If falls of persons from heights or into excavations or holes are involved, state distance of fall in metres							m

GA20 Accident report *continued*

GA

20. What action has been taken to prevent a recurrence?							
21. If machinery was involved							
a) give name and number of machine or part causing the accident							
b) was it working at the time of the accident?					Yes		No
22. Names and addresses of witnesses to the accident. (Always obtain witnesses wherever possible.)							
a)							
b)							
c)							
Attach signed statements from each witness whenever possible.							
23. Use a separate sheet of paper for a sketch plan of the scene.							
Name		Position		Signature		Date	

To be completed by Head Office						
Further medical reports on injured person		Yes		No	Date	
Injured person ceased employment		Yes		No	Date	
New address for injured person						
Is a further investigation report required?				Yes		No
Have control measures been implemented to prevent occurrence?		Yes		No	Date	

GA

GA21 Accident/incident investigation report (Part 1)

Company name		**Project title**	
Location		**Contract no.**	
Date		**Reference no.**	

General location of accident/incident *(tick)*

	Access route		Car park
	At task location whilst undertaking activity		Delivery/storage area
	Loading/unloading area		Office/site offices
	Public highway		Residential dwelling
	Site perimeter/off site		Vehicle
	Welfare site		Other

Date of accident		**Time**	
Injured person's name		**Occupation**	
Address			
Employer		**Supervisor**	
Site manager		**First aider**	

Injury	**Treatment administered** *(on or off site)*

1. Witness		**Employer**	
2. Witness		**Employer**	
3. Witness		**Employer**	

Incident classification *(indicate appropriate category)*

	RIDDOR – Fatal		RIDDOR – Disease		Process interruption
	RIDDOR – Specified injury		Lost time 1 – 7 days		Environmental incident
	RIDDOR – Over seven-day injury		Minor		Environmental near miss
	RIDDOR – Dangerous occurrence		Member of public injury		Significant learning event
	RIDDOR – Injury to member of public		Service strike		Reportable ill health

Previous experience/training of injured person

Relevant training details			
Other *(specify)*			
Date of induction		**Date of last relevant awareness talk(s)**	

GA21 Accident/incident investigation report (Part 1) *continued*

Supporting information available * Digital photographs must have the correct level of validation *(date, independent witness, etc.)*					
	Risk assessment		Witness statement		Other *(state below)*
	Method statement		Site sketch		
	Competency checks/card		Photographs		
	Induction log		Construction drawings		
	Toolbox talk attendance		Maintenance checks (PPM)		
	Injured person's statement		F2508/A		

Date	Time	**Background information:** in date/time order *(to include – start dates, previous works, contract progress, work group personnel, adjacent trades, nature of work being undertaken, etc.)*

Date	Time	**Summary of accident:** in date/time order *(concise description of the incident including location, personnel involved, activity being carried out, tools/equipment/substances involved, permits to work, site drawings and working conditions. Record timeline of events.)*

Immediate action taken: emergency plan, first aid, securing site, hospital, contacts made, prevention of further loss.

Investigation team			
Name	**Position**	**Signature**	**Date**

Investigation approval							
Name		**Position**		**Signature**		**Date**	

Distribution				
Name	**Position**	**Telephone**	**Email**	**Dist. (✓)**

GA

GA22 Accident/incident investigation report (Part 2)

Company name		**Project title**	
Location		**Contract no.**	
Report title		**Report date**	
Accident date		**Accident ref.**	
	Initial report		**Final report**

Immediate cause of accident *(consider all factors, including temperature, weather, system failure, design failure, equipment failure, poor housekeeping and the influence of alcohol or drugs)*
Root cause of accident *(consider issues, such as lack of training and awareness, time constraints, communication and external influences)*
Remedial action *(use continuation sheet if necessary)*
Conclusion and recommendations *(analysis of evidence, comparison with standards, highlight the main issues, who is responsible, and so on)*

GA22 Accident/incident investigation report (Part 2) *continued*

Recommendations
Immediate
Interim
Long-term

Learning opportunities and responsibilities				
Person responsible	**Action**	**Target date**	**Close out date**	**Signature**

Communication of learning *(tick all that apply)*					
	Safety alert		Safety bulletin		Safety briefing
	Toolbox talks		Review of RA/MS		Review of policy and procedures
	Review of training requirements		Other *(state)*		

GA

GA22 Accident/incident investigation report (Part 2) *continued*

Investigation team			
Name	**Position**	**Signature**	**Date**

Investigation approval and distribution			
Name	**Position**	**Signature**	**Date**
	HS&E Department		
	Project manager		
	Project director		
	Managing director		

Appendices	
Supporting information *(tick those appended)*	
Other report forms	
	RIDDOR F2508/A form
	Contractors completed accident book entry form *(where applicable)*
	Contractors completed incident/accident investigation report *(where applicable)*
	Client incident/accident investigation report *(where applicable)*
Witness statements	
	Name
	Title/occupation
	Employer
Photographs	
	Photograph index sheet and photographs
Drawings	
	Scale drawing/plans
	Incident site sketch
Training/control	
	Copy of signed method statement/risk assessment
	Copy of any relevant permits or other work instructions
	Copy of signed induction log
	Last completed toolbox talk or relevant safety briefing
	Copy of relevant skills card (CPCS, CSCS, etc.)

GA23 Witness statement

Company name		**Project title**	
Location		**Contract no.**	
Name of witness		**Date of incident**	
Address			
Occupation			

Statement	**Page**		**of**	

This statement (consisting of pages, each signed by me) is true to the best of my knowledge and belief and I make it knowing that, if it is tendered in evidence, I shall be liable to prosecution if I have wilfully stated in it anything that I know to be false or do not believe to be true.

Name		**Position**		**Signature**		**Date**	
Signature witnessed by							
Name		**Position**		**Signature**		**Date**	

GA

GA24 Enforcement authority visit report

Company name		Project title				
Location		Contract no.				
Site manager						
Person completing report		Date				
Enforcing authority						
Name of inspector(s)						
Office or address						
Contact information						
Reason for visit		Enforcement action taken?		Yes		No

Summary of any enforcement action	Actions taken or to be taken

Summary of inspector's observations	Actions taken or to be taken

Other	

This notification must be issued as soon as practicable after the visit							
Name		Position		Signature		Date	

GA25 Pre-construction information

Description of project	Details
1. Project description and intended use of final structure/building.	
2. Project description and programme details including:	
a) important dates (including planned start and finish of the construction phase)	
b) client's brief.	
3. Extent and location of existing records and plans (such as relevant information from existing health and safety file and asbestos surveys).	
4. Details of:	
a) principal designer	
b) designer(s)	
c) principal contractor	
d) contractor(s)	
e) consultant/others.	
Client's considerations and management requirements	
1. Arrangements for:	
a) planning and managing the construction work, including any health and safety goals for the project	
b) communication and liaison between client and others	
c) time allocated for each stage of the project.	
2. Requirements relating to the health and safety of the client's employees or customers, or other people involved in the project, such as:	
a) security of the site	
b) the requirement for site hoardings	
c) site transport arrangements or restriction on vehicle movements	
d) client permit-to-work systems	
e) fire precautions	
f) emergency procedures and means of escape	
g) 'no-go' areas or other authorisation requirements	
h) any areas designated as a confined space by the client	
i) smoking and parking restrictions	
j) welfare provision.	

GA

GA25 Pre-construction information *continued*

Environmental restrictions and existing on-site risks	
1. Safety hazards, including:	
a) boundaries and access, including temporary access (for example, narrow streets, lack of parking, turning or storage space)	
b) any restrictions on deliveries, waste collection or storage	
c) adjacent land uses (such as schools, railway lines or busy roads)	
d) existing storage of hazardous materials	
e) location of existing services particularly those that are concealed – water, electricity, gas, and so on	
f) ground conditions, underground structures or water courses where this might affect the safe use of plant (such as cranes, or the safety of groundworks)	
g) information on existing structures – stability, structural form, fragile or hazardous materials, anchorage points for fall-arrest systems (particularly where demolition is involved)	
h) previous structural modifications, including weakening or strengthening of the structure (particularly where demolition is involved)	
i) fire damage, ground shrinkage, movement or poor maintenance, which may have adversely affected the structure	
j) any difficulties relating to plant and equipment in the premises (such as overhead gantries whose height restricts access)	
k) health and safety information contained in earlier design, construction or 'as-built' drawings (such as details of pre-stressed or post-tensioned structures).	
2. Health hazards, including:	
a) asbestos, including results of surveys (particularly where refurbishment and/or demolition is involved)	
b) existing storage of hazardous materials	
c) existing structures containing hazardous materials	
d) health risks arising from the client's work.	

Significant design and construction hazards	
1. Significant design assumptions and suggested work methods, sequences or other control measures.	
2. Arrangements for co-ordination of ongoing design work and handling design changes.	
3. Information on significant risks identified during design.	
4. Materials requiring particular precautions.	

Comments							
Name		Position		Signature		Date	

GA26 Construction phase plan

Company name	
Description of project	**Details**
1. Project description and programme details including any important dates.	
2. Details of the project team, including:	
a) client	
b) principal designer	
c) designer(s)	
d) principal contractor	
e) contractor(s)	
f) other consultants.	
3. Extent and location of existing records and plans which are relevant to health and safety on site, including information on existing structures when appropriate.	
Management of the work	
1. Management structure and responsibilities.	
2. Health and safety goals for the project and arrangements for monitoring and review of health and safety performance.	
3. Health and safety arrangements for the construction phase.	
4. Site rules.	
5. Arrangements for:	
a) co-operation between the project team on site and co-ordination of their work	
b) consultation with the workforce	
c) the exchange of design information between the client, designers, principal designers and contractors on site	
d) handling design changes during the project	
e) the selection and control of contractors	
f) the exchange of health and safety information between contractors	

GA

GA26 Construction phase plan *continued*

Management of the work *(continued)*	Details
g) site security	
h) site induction	
i) on-site training	
j) welfare facilities and first aid	
k) the reporting and investigation of accidents and incidents including near misses	
l) the production and approval of risk assessments and written systems of work	
m) fire and emergency procedures.	
Arrangements for controlling significant site risks	
1. Safety risks, including:	
a) delivery and removal of materials (including waste) and work equipment taking account of any risks to the public (for example during access to or egress from the site)	
b) dealing with services – water, electricity and gas, including overhead powerlines and temporary electrical installations	
c) accommodating adjacent land use	
d) stability of structures whilst carrying out construction work, including temporary structures and existing unstable structures	
e) preventing falls	
f) work with or near fragile materials	
g) work involving the assembly or dismantling of heavy, prefabricated components	
h) work near high-voltage cables	
i) work on excavations and work where there are poor ground conditions	
j) work on wells, underground earthworks and tunnels	
k) work exposing workers to the risk of drowning	
l) work carried out by divers having a system of air supply	
m) work in a caisson with a compressed air system	
n) work involving explosives	
o) traffic routes and segregation of vehicles and pedestrians	
p) storage of materials *(particularly hazardous materials)* and work equipment	

GA26 Construction phase plan *continued*

Arrangements for controlling significant site risks *(continued)*	Details
q) work which puts workers at risk from chemical and biological substances	
r) work with ionising radiation requiring the designation of controlled or supplied areas.	
2. Health risks, including:	
a) the removal of asbestos	
b) dealing with contaminated land	
c) manual handling	
d) use of hazardous substances, particularly where there is a need for health monitoring	
e) reducing noise and/or vibration	
f) exposure to UV radiation *(from the sun)*	
g) any other significant health risks.	
The health and safety file	
1. Layout and format.	
2. Arrangements for the collection and gathering of information.	
3. Storage of information.	
Significant design and construction hazards	
1. Significant design assumptions and suggested work methods, sequences or other control measures.	
2. Arrangements for co-ordination of ongoing design work and handling design changes.	
3. Information on significant risks identified during design.	
4. Materials requiring particular precautions.	

Comments							
Name		Position		Signature		Date	

GA

GA27 Health and safety file

It is the responsibility of the principal designer to ensure that a health and safety file is prepared and revised for the project. The file is **only required for projects involving more than one contractor** and should only include information about the current project that is likely to be needed to ensure health and safety during any subsequent work (such as maintenance, cleaning, refurbishment or demolition).

1. A brief description of the work carried out.	
2. Any hazards that have not been eliminated through the design or construction process and how they have been addressed (for example surveys or other information concerning asbestos, contaminated land, water bearing strata and underground services).	
3. Key structural principles (for example bracing, sources of substantial stored energy, including pre- or post-tensioned members) and safe working loads for floors and roofs.	
4. Hazardous materials used (for example lead paint, pesticides and special coatings).	
5. Information regarding the removal or dismantling of installed plant and equipment (for example any special arrangements for lifting such equipment).	
6. Health and safety information about equipment provided for cleaning or maintaining the structure.	
7. The nature, location and markings of significant services, including underground cables, gas supply equipment, fire-fighting services and so on.	
8. Information and as-built drawings of the building, its plant and equipment (for example the means of safe access to and from service voids, fire doors and compartmentalisation and so on).	

Name		**Position**		**Signature**		**Date**	

GB Health and welfare

The contents of this chapter should be read and used in conjunction with guidance contained within Section B.

Contents

GB01 Skin protection checklist

Company name		Project title	
Location		Contract no.	

Protection of the skin

	Yes	No
1. Have the materials or substances in use been identified?		
2. Is up to date manufacturers' information available on the safe use of the substances?		
3. Have the hazardous substances that will be produced by a work process been identified?		
4. Have the necessary risk assessments been carried out?		
5. Has an attempt been made to control the hazard at source (for example, by using a less hazardous substance)?		
6. Has a COSHH assessment been carried out for the substances in use?		
7. Have the significant findings of the COSHH assessment been communicated to those who will be using or otherwise affected by the substance?		
8. Are the correct warning and cautionary notices displayed?		
9. Are the methods of handling, transport and storage correct for the substances being used?		
10. Are there adequate selection and training procedures available for operatives using harmful substances?		
11. Is it necessary for workers to have wet hands for long periods or repeatedly get their hands wet?		
12. Have operatives been properly trained in the necessary precautions and protective measures required for safe working?		
13. Are safe working procedures and methods being properly implemented?		
14. Is the correct handling equipment available and in use?		
15. Is there adequate ventilation where toxic materials are in use?		
16. Are there adequate washing facilities, barrier creams and cleansing agents of the correct type available and in regular use?		
17. Are there gloves and protective clothing of the correct type and specification available and in use?		
18. Have they been selected by a competent person, who can be the supplier?		
19. Is there provision for cleaning protective clothing?		
20. Is protective clothing regularly changed?		
21. Are there adequate supervision and inspection procedures in place?		
22. Is medical surveillance available for operatives, when applicable?		
23. Have appropriate welfare and first-aid facilities been provided?		
24. Other *(please state)*		

Comments

Name		Position		Signature		Date	

GB

GB02 Lead hazards checklist

Company name		Project title	
Location		Contract no.	

Lead hazards

	Yes	No
1. Have you been provided with a copy of the lead survey report and/or lead register?		
2. Has a suitable and sufficient risk assessment been carried out?		
3. Have all persons who have to work with lead received adequate information, instruction and training?		
4. Has the HSE publication *Lead and you* been issued to all employees?		
5. Has the nature and extent of any exposure to lead been assessed?		
6. Has the monitoring of lead in air levels been carried out?		
7. Is medical surveillance of individuals (which includes checking blood-lead levels before the works) necessary and, if so, undertaken?		
8. Should blood-lead levels be determined from a blood sample or a saliva check?		
9. If medical surveillance is necessary, are medical records kept as required?		
10. Are measures in place to control levels of exposure to lead?		
11. Is protective equipment and clothing in use, as necessary and required?		
12. Is the correct type of respiratory equipment being used for the hazard being encountered?		
13. Are measures being taken to control the spread of any lead contamination and how is this being checked (for example, dust-wipe sampling)?		
14. Is there adequate provision of washing and changing facilities?		
15. Are separate areas provided for eating and drinking?		
16. Are all operatives adequately trained in safe working procedures?		
17. Are operatives aware of the risks to health that can arise from not working safely?		
18. Are records being kept as required by the relevant regulations?		
19. Are arrangements in place to deal with accidents, incidents and emergency?		

Comments

Name		Position		Signature		Date	

GB

GB03 Lead-containing paint risk assessment

This form is split into three sections.

1. Lead-containing paint risk assessment details

Company name		**Project title**	
Location		**Contract no.**	
Document ref no.		**Assessment date**	
Issue date		**Originator**	
Review date		**Responsibility**	

Lead-containing paint hazard *(Hazard location – room reference)*	**Who may be harmed?** *(List those at risk)*	**Is risk adequately controlled?** *(List existing controls)*	**Further action required to control risk** *(List further action to be taken and cross-reference to manager's action plan)*	**Review dates**

Comments

GB

GB03 Lead-containing paint risk assessment *continued*

2. Lead-containing paint risk assessment record

This document is an easy-to use checklist to allow a **suitable and sufficient assessment of the risk to health and safety** arising from the proposed works likely to involve the disturbance or removal of lead-containing paint.

Full completion of this sheet is not a legal requirement.

Hazard location		Room reference						
Description	**Reference**	**Lead check?**		**Lead hazard?**		**Lab check?**		**Lead amount**
		Yes	**No**	**Yes**	**No**	**Yes**	**No**	
Floors								
Floor voids								
Walls								
Skirtings								
Panelling								
Dado rails								
Picture rails								
Windows								
Cills								
Sub-cills								
Windowboards								
Pelmets								
Curtain rails								
Shutters								
Fanlights								
Doors								
Frames								
Linings								
Stops								
Architraves								
Stairs								
Stair treads								
Newel posts								
Spindles								
Stringers								
Spandrel panels								
Miscellaneous								
Access hatches								
Meter cupboards								
Roof access/ceiling voids								
Floor access/floor voids								
Cellar access								
Boxed-in pipework/services								
Beams/columns								
Beneath asbestos fireproofing								
Fascias/soffits								
Fitted components								
Cupboards								
Fireplace surrounds								
Tank/boiler housings								
Architectural details								
Behind dry lining and false or suspended ceilings								
Other								

GB03 Lead-containing paint risk assessment *continued*

3. Lead-containing paint risk assessment record (manager's action plan)

Manager's name						
Department/location						
Further action identified from risk assessment	**No action to be taken/risk accepted**		**Person responsible to carry out action**	**Date by which action is to be completed**	**Review date of action** *(comments)*	**Date of action completed, signature of manager**
	Yes	**No**				
1.						
2.						
3.						
4.						
5.						
6.						

Comments							
Name		**Position**		**Signature**		**Date**	

GB

GB04 Lead health surveillance record

Recorded details of an employee under medical surveillance because of exposure to lead (Regulation 10 Control of Lead at Work Regulations).

Employee's details	
Surname	
Forenames	
Maiden name (if applicable)	
Permanent address	
Place of birth	
Date of birth	
Sex	
N.I. number	
NHS number (if available)	

Doctor's (GP) details	
Name	
Address	
Telephone number	
Fax number (if any)	

Employer's details	
Name	
Address	
Telephone number	
Email	
Standard Industrial Classification (SIC numbor)	

Employment details	
Years exposed to lead before starting in current employment	
Date of first exposure to lead in current employment (Day Month Year)	
Date of end of exposure to lead in current employment (Day Month Year)	

Additional information	
The reason for medical surveillance	
The dates of initial and periodic medical surveillance	
The results of clinical assessments	
The results of measuring blood-lead concentrations and of any other biological tests in enough detail to allow adverse trends to be identified	
Action taken, including periods moved to work not involving exposure to lead, and periods of suspension	

GB05 Initial hand-arm vibration screening questionnaire

Medical in confidence – when completed

Initial screening questionnaire for workers using hand-held vibrating tools, hand-guided vibrating machines and hand-fed vibrating machines.

GB

Company name		**Project title**	
Location		**Contract no.**	

Date	
Employee name	
Occupation	
Address	
Date of birth	
National insurance number	
Employer name	

1. Have you ever used hand-held vibrating tools, machines or hand-fed processes in your job?		Yes		No
If 'Yes': **a) list year of first exposure**				
b) when was the last time you used them? *(detail work history overleaf)*				
2. Do you have any tingling of the fingers lasting more than 20 minutes after using vibration equipment?		Yes		No
3. Do you have tingling of the fingers at any other time?		Yes		No
4. Do you wake at night with pain, tingling, or numbness in your hand or wrist?		Yes		No
5. Do one or more of your fingers go numb more than 20 minutes after using vibration equipment?		Yes		No
6. Have your fingers gone white* on cold exposure?		Yes		No
If 'Yes', do you have difficulty re-warming them when leaving the cold?		Yes		No
7. Do your fingers go white at any other time?		Yes		No
8. Are you experiencing any other problems with the muscles or joints of the hands or arms?		Yes		No
9. Do you have difficulty picking up very small objects (for example screws or buttons) or opening tight jars?		Yes		No
10. Have you ever had a neck, arm or hand injury or operation? If 'Yes' give details below.		Yes		No
11. Have you ever had any serious diseases of joints, skin, nerves, heart or blood vessels? If 'Yes' give details below.		Yes		No
12. Are you on any long-term medication? If 'Yes' give details below.		Yes		No

** Whiteness means a clear discoloration of the fingers with a sharp edge, usually followed by a red flush.*

GB05 Initial hand-arm vibration screening questionnaire *continued*

Occupational history	
Dates	**Job title**

I certify that all the answers given are true to the best of my knowledge and belief.

Name		Position		Signature		Date	

Return in confidence to

(Reproduced from the HSE publication Hand-arm vibration (L140) under licence from The Controller of Her Majesty's Stationery Office.)

GB06 COSHH management action plan checklist

Company name		**Project title**	
Location		**Contract no.**	

COSHH management action plan

	Yes	No	N/A
1. Compile inventory of all hazardous substances, to which employees may be exposed, which are either purchased (proprietary products), created by a work process (dust and fumes) or may be already on site (micro-organisms, contaminated land and residues).			
2. Gather relevant technical information about each substance from sources such as labelling, safety data sheets, the HSE website and trade organisations.			
3. For each substance above, evaluate the work task(s) and working practices associated with it. If necessary, observe the work activity in which the hazardous substance is used or created.			
4. From information and observations made, decide if there are any risks to health.			
5. Assess what action needs to be taken to prevent exposure (priority), or to control it to an acceptable level.			
6. Record the significant findings of the assessment.			
7. Take the actions necessary to ensure that the appropriate control measures are provided, properly used and maintained as necessary.			
8. Provide all users of (or those creating) each hazardous substance with the necessary information, instruction and training.			
9. From the information gained, decide if there is any requirement for exposure monitoring and health surveillance.			
10. Review the assessment regularly and revise it as necessary.			

Comments

Name		**Position**		**Signature**		**Date**	

GB07 COSHH assessment

Name of hazardous substance	
Substance hazard classification	
Trade name(s)	
Substance used for	
Likely circumstances of exposure	

Potential hazards	Risk control measures	Emergency procedures
Inhalation can lead to nausea and headaches.		
Skin contact can be irritating and have a defatting effect. Can cause contact or irritant dermatitis.		
Eye contact will cause irritation.		
Ingestion will irritate mouth, throat, and so on.		
Fire: flammable liquid. Products of combustion are toxic. Vapour/air mixture is explosive.		
Spillage: fumes/ vapour likely to collect in low areas.		

Additional information.

Are current controls adequate? Yes/No

Assessment date		**Next review date**	
Approved for use by			

Name		**Position**		**Signature**		**Date**	

GB08 Annual hand-arm vibration questionnaire

Health surveillance questionnaire for workers using hand-held vibrating tools, hand-guided vibrating machines and hand-fed vibrating machines.

Company name		**Project title**	
Location		**Contract no.**	

Date	
Employee name	
Occupation	
Address	
Date of birth	
National insurance number	
Employer name	
Date of previous screening	

Have you been using hand-held vibrating tools, machines or hand-fed processes in your job, or if this is a review, since your last assessment? *(detail work history overleaf)*		Yes		No
If 'No' or more than two years since last exposure, please return the form – there is no need to answer any further questions.				
If 'Yes'				
1. Do you have any numbness or tingling of the fingers lasting more than 20 minutes after using vibrating equipment?		Yes		No
2. Do you have numbness or tingling of the fingers at any other time?		Yes		No
3. Do you wake at night with pain, tingling or numbness in your hand or wrist?		Yes		No
4. Have any of your fingers gone white* on cold exposure?		Yes		No
5. Have you noticed any change in your response to your tolerance of working outdoors in the cold?		Yes		No
6. Are you experiencing any other problems in your hands or arms?		Yes		No
7. Do you have difficulty in picking up very small objects (for example, screws or buttons) or opening tight jars?		Yes		No
8. Has anything changed about your health since the last assessment?		Yes		No
** Whiteness means a clear discoloration of the fingers with a sharp edge, usually followed by a red flush.*				
I certify that all the answers given above are true to the best of my knowledge and belief.				

Name		**Position**		**Signature**		**Date**	

Return to

GB08 Annual hand-arm vibration questionnaire *continued*

Hand-arm vibration syndrome (HAVS):

- ☑ is a disorder that affects the blood vessels, nerves, muscles and joints of the hand, wrist and arm
- ☑ can become severely disabling if ignored; and
- ☑ its best known form is vibration white finger (VWF), which can be triggered by cold or wet weather and can cause severe pain in the affected fingers.

Signs to look out for in hand-arm vibration syndrome:

- ☑ tingling and numbness in the fingers
- ☑ in the cold and wet, fingers go white, then blue, then red and are painful
- ☑ you can't feel things with your fingers
- ☑ pain, tingling or numbness in your hands, wrists and arms
- ☑ loss of strength in hands.

Occupational history							
Dates		**Job title**					
Name		**Position**		**Signature**		**Date**	

(Reproduced from the HSE publication Hand-arm vibration (L140) under licence from The Controller of Her Majesty's Stationery Office.)

GB

GB09 Whole-body vibration health monitoring questionnaire

Company name		**Project title**	
Location		**Contract no.**	

Date of assessment	
Employee number/Payroll number	
Name	
Date of birth	
Job title	

Any change in duties since last questionnaire?		Yes		No
Recent experience				
Is there currently any movement or activity that causes you pain in your back?		Yes		No
Have you suffered any back/neck/shoulder pain in the last 12 months?		Yes		No
Please describe the severity of the pain experienced *(tick below)*				

No pain										Pain as bad as it could be
0	1	2	3	4	5	6	7	8	9	10

Note: *if severity above 5 is indicated, refer on for further advice. However if rank less than 5, but for three consecutive assessments, then refer for further advice. (Further advice should be sought from an occupational health professional or GP in these cases.)*

Have you had to take any medication to deal with the pain experienced?		Yes		No
Have you had to seek medical advice regarding this pain?		Yes		No
Has this back/neck/shoulder pain resulted in time off work?		Yes		No
Have you had any accidents or injury to your back in the last two years?		Yes		No
Action/advice				
Referral for further advice?		Yes		No
Other advice provided?		Yes		No

Employee							
Name		**Position**		**Signature**		**Date**	
Assessor							
Name		**Position**		**Signature**		**Date**	

(Reproduced from the HSE publication Whole-body vibration (L141) under licence from The Controller of Her Majesty's Stationery Office.)

GB10 Hand-arm vibration syndrome assessment

Company name		**Project title**	
Location		**Contract no.**	
Assessor		**Person being assessed**	
Occupation			

How many years have you been in this job?	
How many years have you been using hand-held vibration tools?	
How many days per week do you use hand-held vibration tools?	
Approximately how many hours per day do you use hand-held vibration tools? (Time spent when trigger pressed – not including time holding tool when trigger is not pressed)	

Are you *(tick)*		Left-handed		Right-handed

Which vibratory tools have been used most frequently during your career? *(Tick below)*

	1. Road breaker		2. Chipping hammer		3. Compactor plate
	4. Poker		5. Drills		6. Grinder or disc cutter
	7. Strimmer		8. Scabbler		9. Other *(please state)*

Do you wear gloves to keep your hands warm when using vibrating tools?		**Always**		**Sometimes**		**Never**
Do your fingers go white in cold weather and are slow to return to normal?		**Always**		**Sometimes**		**Never**
Have you noticed any tingling in your fingers that lasts more than a few minutes after using vibrating tools?		**Always**		**Sometimes**		**Never**
Have you ever noticed your fingers go numb in cold weather and are slow to return to normal?		**Always**		**Sometimes**		**Never**

Do you have any problems with the joints or muscles of your hands or arms, such as the following *(tick all that apply)*

	Pain		Swelling		Stiffness		Weakness
	Fine movements		Other *(please state)*				

State trigger times for Items being used *(include make of model)*

Equipment	**Trigger M/s**	**Equipment**	**Trigger M/s**	**Equipment**	**Trigger M/s**	**Equipment**	**Trigger M/s**
Breaker (heavy)		4" grinder		Drill (heavy)		Other	
Drill (small)		8" grinder		Rip saw		**State duration of use below**	
Stilh		110 v breaker		Jigsaw		Hrs	Mins

State further mitigation measures required to eliminate/reduce hand-arm vibration syndrome exposure (such as job rotation, alternative working, newer equipment, and so on)

I understand the content and importance of the assessment and I have answered the above questions to the best of my knowledge. I agree to comply with the stated exposure duration that I understand must not be exceeded.

I give permission for my employer to pass on my completed hand-arm vibration syndrome assessment to my employer's external occupational health physician for evaluation purposes, if deemed appropriate.

Assessor							
Name		**Position**		**Signature**		**Date**	
Assessed							
Name		**Position**		**Signature**		**Date**	

GB

GB11 Manual handling checklist

The following can be used as a checklist when developing safe systems of work.

Company name		Project title	
Location		Contract no.	

Manual handling

Preparation	Yes	No
1. What is being lifted?		
2. Where to and how far?		
3. Has a manual handling risk assessment been carried out?		
4. Would mechanical means be more practical or appropriate?		
5. Is the operation part of a routine? If so, could it be more effectively planned and executed?		
6. How many people will be needed to move the load safely?		
7. Are they all trained in kinetic lifting and handling?		
8. Are proper (kinetic) lifting methods being employed?		
9. What methods and equipment will be required?		
10. Is the required equipment available?		
11. Is the lifting and handling area clear of hazards?		
Lifting and handling	**Yes**	**No**
12. Is the proper personal protective clothing in use?		
13. Is co-ordination satisfactory in dual and team lifting with one person taking charge of the lift?		
14. Is the necessary equipment in use or to hand?		
15. Are excessively heavy weights being lifted?		
16. Are loads being deposited or stacked safely and securely?		
17. Is adequate supervision employed where necessary?		
After lifting and handling	**Yes**	**No**
18. Has there been any past incidents or accidents?		
19. Is there anything to be learnt from them to avoid similar incidents happening again?		
20. Did anyone receive an injury and does this need to be taken into account for future tasks?		
21. Has any damage or loss of equipment been recorded and repaired/replaced?		

Comments

Name		Position		Signature		Date	

GB12 Manual handling assessment

Section A – Preliminary

Company name		Project title	
Location		Contract no.	

Task name	
Task description	
Load weight	
Frequency of lift	
Carry distances (if applicable)	

Are other manual handling tasks carried out by these operators?		Yes		No
Assessment discussed with employees/safety representatives		Yes		No
Is an assessment needed? (Tick)		Yes*		No

** An assessment will be needed if there is a potential risk of injury (such as if the task falls outside the guidelines)*
If 'Yes' continue. If 'No' the assessment need go no further.

Operations covered by this assessment *(detailed description)*

Locations	
Personnel involved	
Date of assessment	

Diagrams *(other information, including existing control measures)*

Overall assessment of the risk of injury*?		Low		Medium		High

** Make your overall assessment* ***after*** *you have completed Section B.*

(Reproduced from Guidance on The Manual Handling Operations Regulations under licence from Her Majesty's Stationery Office.)

GB12 Manual handling assessment *continued*

GB

Section B – Lifting and carrying – more detailed assessment, where necessary

Questions to consider	If yes, tick appropriate level of risk			Problems occurring from the task	Possible remedial action *(such as changes to be made to the task, load, working environment, etc.)*
	Low	Med	High		
Do the tasks involve:					
■ holding loads away from trunk?					
■ twisting?					
■ stooping?					
■ reaching upwards?					
■ large vertical movement?					
■ long carrying distances?					
■ strenuous pushing or pulling?					
■ unpredictable movement of loads?					
■ repetitive handling?					
■ insufficient rest or recovery?					
■ a work rate imposed by a process?					
Are the loads:					
■ heavy?					
■ bulky/unwieldy?					
■ difficult to grasp?					
■ unstable/unpredictable?					
■ intrinsically harmful (for example, sharp/hot)?					
Consider the working environment – are there:					
■ constraints on posture?					
■ poor floors?					
■ variations in levels?					

GB12 Manual handling assessment *continued*

Questions to consider	If yes, tick appropriate level of risk			Problems occurring from the task	Possible remedial action *(such as changes to be made to the task, load, working environment, etc.)*
	Low	Med	High		
Consider the working environment – are there *continued*:					
■ hot/cold/humid conditions?					
■ strong air movements?					
■ poor lighting conditions?					
Consider individual capability – does the job:					
■ require unusual capability?					
■ pose a risk to those with a health problem or a physical or learning difficulty?					
■ pose a risk to those who are pregnant?					
■ call for special information/ training?					
Other factors to consider					
Protective clothing					
■ Is movement or posture hindered by clothing or personal protective equipment (PPE)?					
■ Is there an absence of the correct/suitable PPE being worn?					
Work organisation (psychosocial factors)					
■ Do workers feel that there has been a lack of consideration given to the planning and scheduling of tasks/rest breaks?					
■ Do workers feel that there is poor communication between managers and employees (not involved in risk assessments or decisions on changes in workstation design)?					
■ Are there sudden changes in workload, or seasonal changes in volume without mechanisms for dealing with the change?					
■ Do workers feel they have not been given enough training and information to carry out the task successfully?					

(Reproduced from Guidance on The Manual Handling Operations Regulations under licence from Her Majesty's Stationery Office.)

GB12 Manual handling assessment *continued*

Section C – Remedial action to be taken

Remedial steps that should be taken, in order of priority	Person responsible for implementing controls	Target implementation date	Completed	
			Yes	No
1.				
2.				
3.				
4.				
5.				
6.				
7.				
8.				
9.				
Date by which actions should be completed				
Date for review of assessment				

Name		Position		Signature		Date	

(Reproduced from Guidance on The Manual Handling Operations Regulations under licence from Her Majesty's Stationery Office.)

Take action… and check that it has the desired effect.

GC

General safety

The contents of this chapter should be read and used in conjunction with guidance contained within Section C.

Contents

GC01 Site organisation checklist

Company name		**Project title**	
Location		**Contract no.**	

Overview

What you need to know

In order that a construction site can be set up correctly to meet the requirements of the size and complexity of the project, there are many factors to be taken into consideration. The checklists below identify some of the significant hazards and risks to be considered.

What you need to do

Use the information detailed in the construction phase plan to tailor the site set up to meet the needs of the construction project (for example, existing building(s), contamination and demolition).

Significant hazards and risks

Safety	**Yes**	**No**	**N/A**
1. Can a safe working area be provided, with pedestrians and vehicles segregated?			
2. Is there a secure working area, areas for storage of materials and for waste skips with suitable access for deliveries and removals?			
3. Are there adequate emergency escape routes from all areas of the site?			
4. Is there a suitable fire plan, sounder, fire extinguishers and communication?			
5. Are there rescue plans for high risk activities (such as excavations and work at height)?			
Health	**Yes**	**No**	**N/A**
6. Has an adequate risk assessment been prepared for the tasks to be undertaken?			
7. Have welfare facilities been arranged for the site – suitable for tasks/number of workers anticipated and available from day one?			
8. Are there any hazardous substances being used – COSHH?			
9. What measures will be put in place to prevent or minimise all work activities which create dust?			
Environment	**Yes**	**No**	**N/A**
10. Are there any watercourses or other potential pollution receptors nearby?			
11. Does any wildlife need to be considered?			
12. Is there potential for contaminated land?			
13. Is there potential for pollution by the work activity (such as spills, noise, dust and light, provision of spill kits)?			
Managerial/supervisory tasks (including pre-planning)	**Yes**	**No**	**N/A**
14. Has the construction phase plan been prepared and approved for work to begin?			
15. Have the risk assessments been reviewed and found to be task/site specific?			
16. Has a traffic management plan been prepared, with pedestrian segregation?			
17. Is the level of supervision and monitoring of work sufficient?			
Training/competency requirements	**Yes**	**No**	**N/A**
18. Have competency assessments been undertaken for contractors being used?			
19. Do the supervisors and workers have the requisite skills and training records for the tasks to be undertaken?			
20. Do supervisors and workers hold any required competency card (such as CPCS, CSCS and/or alternative schemes)?			

GC01 Site organisation checklist *continued*

Significant hazards and risks *continued*

Safe systems of work/basic control measures	Yes	No	N/A
21. Have high risk activities been identified, and risk controls minimised to an acceptable level? Do they include risks to those putting in control measures (such as those erecting edge protection)?			
22. Have the method statements and risk assessments been approved prior to contractors commencing on site?			
23. Is there a procedure to update documentation during the works, which should be detailed as part of a competency check?			
24. Are employees empowered to take action if they feel additional control measures are needed and are there measures in place for effective worker engagement?			
Specific regulatory or special requirements	**Yes**	**No**	**N/A**
25. Are there registers on site for statutory inspections (such as scaffolding or excavations)?			
26. Are there any high risk activities that may require rescue plans (such as work at height)?			
27. Have electrical installations been completed by competent contractors and tested?			

Comments

Name		Position		Signature		Date	

GC02 Fire risk management checklist

This checklist has been produced as an aide memoire for those with on-site responsibility for fire safety.

For further information refer to the Health and Safety Executive (HSE) and the Fire Protection Association.

Company name		Project title	
Location		Contract no.	

Overview

What you need to know

You must be aware of the fire risk arising out of the materials and substances that are stored and used on site, should they come into contact with a source of ignition.

What you need to do

- ☑ Assess the fire risks and update them periodically as the project progresses and on-site conditions change.
- ☑ Take into account any existing third-party arrangements and others who may be put at risk by fire. Put in place control measures that eliminate the risk of fire or reduce it to an acceptable level.
- ☑ Communicate the significant fire risks and the preventative measures to all on site.

Significant hazards and risks

Safety	Yes	No	N/A
1. Is there a risk of burns from coming into contact with fire?			
2. Is there a risk of slips, trips and falls during rapid site evacuation?			
3. Is there a risk of spread of fire to third-party buildings or areas?			
Health	**Yes**	**No**	**N/A**
4. Is there a risk of inhalation of smoke and toxic fumes (both on and off site)?			
Environment	**Yes**	**No**	**N/A**
5. Is there a risk of fire-fighting water run-off entering watercourses?			
6. Is there a risk of emission of noxious and toxic fumes?			
7. Is there a risk of ground contamination from products of combustion?			
Managerial/supervisory tasks (including pre-planning)	**Yes**	**No**	**N/A**
8. Have the fire risks been assessed and effective control measures put in place?			
9. Has a fire action plan been compiled?			
10. Have you liaised with the Fire and Rescue Service?			
11. Has unauthorised access to the site been prevented?			
Training/competency requirements	**Yes**	**No**	**N/A**
12. Has fire safety been included as part of induction and refresher training?			
13. Has training been provided for anyone with specific fire safety duties?			
14. Has training been provided on the selection and use of fire extinguishers for some staff?			
Safe systems of work/basic control measures	**Yes**	**No**	**N/A**
15. Have flammable materials been stored safely?			
16. Has particular attention been paid to the safe storage and use of flammable and explosive gases?			
17. Have hot-work permits for higher risk activities been implemented?			

GC02 Fire risk management checklist *continued*

Significant hazards and risks *continued*			
Specific regulatory or special requirements	**Yes**	**No**	**N/A**
18. Is everyone competent to do what is asked of them with regard to fire safety?			
19. Has it been established who is the responsible person with regard to fire safety?			
Comments			

Name		Position		Signature		Date	

GC03 Example of a fire risk assessment

There are five steps to fire prevention and control.

1. **Identify hazards.** Consider how a fire could start and what could burn.
2. **People at risk.** Employees, contractors, visitors and anyone who is vulnerable (for example, people nearby or anyone with a disability).
3. **Evaluation and action.** Consider the hazards and people identified in Steps 1 and 2 and act to remove and reduce risk to protect people and premises.
4. **Record, plan and train.** Keep a record of the risks and action taken. Make a clear plan for fire safety and ensure that people understand what they need to do in the event of a fire.
5. **Review** your assessment regularly and check it takes account of any changes on site.

Company name		**Project title**	
Location		**Contract no.**	
Risk assessment reference			
Issue date		**Review date**	
Activity specific details (for example, site locations/activities/zones)			
Other work being carried out in this area			
Interfaces with other trades			
Period of validity of this risk assessment			
Start date		**Expiry date**	
Remember: all hot works must cease at least one hour before the site closes (or more depending upon the risk assessment, as defined in HSG168)			

GC03 Example of a fire risk assessment *continued*

Step 1. Identify the hazards. Consider how a fire could start and what could burn.

Sources of ignition *(Hot works, faulty electrical equipment, uncontrolled smoking)*	**Sources of fuel** *(Untidy site, off-cuts, paper, wrappings)*	**Areas of particular risk** *(Near site boundary, waste skips, hot work areas)*

Step 2. Identify the people at risk. Employees, contractors, visitors and anyone who is vulnerable (for example, people nearby or anyone with a disability).

Step 3. Evaluation and action. Consider the hazards and people identified in Steps 1 and 2 and act to remove and reduce risk to protect people and premises.

Step 4. Record, plan and train. Keep a record of the risks and action taken. Make a clear plan for fire safety and ensure that people understand what they need to do in the event of a fire.

Checklist	**Tick**
Fire plan prepared and made known to all who may be affected.	
Record hazards and risks and keep under constant review.	
Record actions taken to reduce hazards and risks to lowest level.	
Select suitable people and arrange for training and updates for people involved.	
Practise alarm and evacuation procedures.	
Put plan in place to measure and correct defects from lessons learned.	
Plan for rewarding good performance awareness and good housekeeping.	

GC03 Example of a fire risk assessment *continued*

Step 5. Assessment review. You must review and record your assessment regularly and check it takes account of any changes on site.		
Review dates	**Completed by**	**Signature**
Review of outcomes – lessons learnt and control measures put in place		
Fire action plan status/currency *(Check current issue displayed)*		
Latest issue date of fire plan		

Name		**Position**		**Signature**		**Date**	

GC04 Example of a fire risk management action plan

Company name		Project title	
Location		Contract no.	
Date of previous review		Carried out by	
Current revision no.		Date of next review	

Risk management

Unacceptable fire risk	Corrective action required	Action by (person)	Action by (date)

Name		Position		Signature		Date	

GC05 Fire evacuation and escape checklist

Company name		Project title	
Location		Contract no.	

Overview

What you need to know

- ☑ The danger to people on site from not being able to escape to a place of safety within a reasonable time.
- ☑ Where, when, what type and in what quantities flammable and highly flammable materials will be stored and used on site – the 'high risk periods'.
- ☑ How many people would have to evacuate the site at any one time and from which locations.

What you need to do

As part of the fire action plan, develop an emergency evacuation plan and keep it up to date, which should include:

- ☑ identifying one or more assembly points
- ☑ an effective method of detecting fires and raising the alarm
- ☑ an effective method of accounting for all who are on site, and instructing them what to do next, when they get to the assembly point
- ☑ providing appropriate and adequate fire-fighting equipment, at suitable locations, and training sufficient people to use it
- ☑ making a commitment to use site inductions to promote the plan and to communicate changes to it to those on site at the time
- ☑ deciding how to co-ordinate an evacuation where only part of the site has to be evacuated or, where the site is in premises, parts of which are occupied by others
- ☑ periodically practising the emergency evacuation of the site to confirm the adequacy of the plan and highlight shortcomings
- ☑ liaising with the local Fire and Rescue Service as necessary
- ☑ compartmentalising the partially finished structure to prevent or slow the spread of fire
- ☑ nominating fire wardens whose job would be to ensure and confirm that their area of responsibility is clear of people when an evacuation takes place
- ☑ paying due regard to the adequacy of fire escape routes.

Escape routes must be:

- ☑ adequate in number and size for the number of people likely to use them (specialist advice might be needed)
- ☑ clearly designated by signage complying with the Health and Safety (Safety Signs and Signals Regulations), particularly at changes of direction and level
- ☑ lit (including standby emergency lighting) if it is possible that they could be used when there is insufficient natural light
- ☑ not obstructed; if work is necessary that unavoidably blocks an escape route, an alternative route must be designated throughout the duration of the work, adjusted if necessary as construction progresses and inspected at least once a week.

Significant hazards and risks

Safety	Yes	No	N/A
1. Is there a danger of fatalities if people are unable to escape in time to a place of safety?			
2. Is there a risk of slips, trip and falls possibly resulting in crush injuries in the rush to escape?			
Health	**Yes**	**No**	**N/A**
3. Is there a risk of burns and other heat-related injuries resulting from contact with fire or hot surfaces/atmospheres?			
4. Is there a risk of respiratory problems resulting from inhalation of smoke and other toxic gases?			
Environment	**Yes**	**No**	**N/A**
5. Are there any issues directly related to emergency evacuation?			

GC05 Fire evacuation and escape checklist *continued*

Significant hazards and risks *continued*			
Managerial/supervisory tasks (including pre-planning)	**Yes**	**No**	**N/A**
6. Has an effective emergency evacuation plan been developed that identifies emergency escape routes and any changes to them?			
7. Has at least one assembly point been identified?			
8. Have the escape routes and assembly points been publicised through induction and refresher training?			
9. Have the escape routes and assembly points been indicated with signs (illuminated if necessary)?			
10. Have practice evacuations been held? (Even a pre-notified practice evacuation is better than none.)			
Training/competency requirements	**Yes**	**No**	**N/A**
11. Is the person managing the fire risks aware of the location and type of hazards at all times and are they competent to develop an effective emergency escape plan?			
12. Have individuals been made aware of, through site induction and refresher training, the risk of fire and what to do if a fire occurs?			
13. Has specific training been provided for those with specific duties (such as fire wardens)?			
Safe systems of work/basic control measures	**Yes**	**No**	**N/A**
14. Are escape routes adequate for the maximum number of people, well signed, lit where necessary and their location publicised during induction and refresher training?			
15. Have the required amount of assembly points been published and are people aware what to do when they get there?			
16. Have practise evacuations been carried out?			
17. Have the time of the evacuation and people's behaviour been monitored?			
18. Has the effectiveness and accuracy of roll calls been established?			
Specific regulatory or special requirements	**Yes**	**No**	**N/A**
19. Has a responsible person, who carries the burden of ensuring that fire risks are adequately managed, been appointed in accordance with fire safety law?			
20. Is the responsible person someone senior within the company who may delegate the day-to-day responsibility for fire safety to a site manager?			

Further information
HSE publication *Fire safety in construction* (HSG168).
Fire Protection Association publication *Fire prevention on construction sites, Code of Practice and checklist.*

Comments

Name		Position		Signature		Date	

GC06 Managing hot work checklist

This checklist has been produced as an aide memoire for those with on-site responsibility for fire safety.

For further information refer to the Health and Safety Executive (HSE) and the Fire Protection Association.

Company name		Project title	
Location		Contract no.	

Overview

What you need to know

You must determine if any particular tasks represent an enhanced risk of fire breaking out due to the use of a source of heat.

What you need to do

- ☑ Establish a hot-work permit system and ensure that it is complied with.
- ☑ Put in place additional controls for higher risk work.

Significant hazards and risks

Safety	Yes	No	N/A
1. Is there a risk of burns from coming into contact with fire?			
2. Is there a risk of injuries to others, who are off site and not prepared, if the fire spreads?			
Health	**Yes**	**No**	**N/A**
3. Is there a risk of inhalation of smoke and other toxic fumes?			
Environment	**Yes**	**No**	**N/A**
4. Is there a risk of fire-fighting water run-off entering watercourses?			
5. Is there a risk of emission of noxious and toxic fumes?			
6. Is there a risk of ground contamination from products of combustion?			
Managerial/supervisory tasks (including pre-planning)	**Yes**	**No**	**N/A**
7. Has it been determined which tasks warrant being carried out under a hot-work permit?			
8. Has compliance with the hot-work permit system been physically monitored?			
9. Does work cease at least one hour before the end of the working day?			
10. Is additional time allowed (two hours) for high risk activity work (such as timber frames)?			
11. Are hot-work activities co-ordinated when more than one are taking place at the same time?			
Training/competency requirements	**Yes**	**No**	**N/A**
12. Have those who carry out hot work been trained on how to use the permit system?			
13. Have others, who are not involved, been told to keep clear of the area?			
Safe systems of work/basic control measures	**Yes**	**No**	**N/A**
14. Is hot work carried out in accordance with the conditions stipulated in the hot-work permit?			
15. Is anyone who is not involved kept out of the area (using physical barriers, if required)?			
16. Is the correct fire extinguisher to hand?			
17. Have third parties been contacted if hot works could interfere with existing fire detection systems?			
Specific regulatory or special requirements	**Yes**	**No**	**N/A**
18. Is everyone competent to do what is asked of them with regard to fire safety?			
19. Has it been established who is the responsible person with regard to fire safety?			

GC06 Managing hot work checklist *continued*

Comments							
Name		Position		Signature		Date	

GC07 Hot-work permit

Hot-work permits are required for any operation involving open flames or producing heat and/or sparks and must be prepared by a competent person. Hot works include brazing, torch cutting, grinding, soldering and welding.

Company name			**Project title**		
Location			**Contract no.**		
Supervisor			**Permit no.**		
Contractor					
Equipment used					
Date of works		**between**	hrs	**and**	hrs

Precautions to be taken	Yes	No	N/A
Hot work must **cease** at least one hour before end of shift.			
Services affected must be **isolated** before work commences.			
Isolate smoke detectors in vicinity of hot works.			
A suitable fire extinguisher must be available and be kept close at hand, at all times.			
Supervisor must ensure suitable personal protective equipment is provided and **worn** by operative.			
All cylinders must be transported and secured **upright**.			
Valves and hoses **must** be in good condition.			
All cylinders must have **flash back** arrestors fitted.			
When not in use cylinders must be **shut off** and returned to store.			
LPG cylinders must **not** be **left in the building** overnight without formal approval.			
Arc welding equipment will comply with current standards.			
Spent welding rods **must be** immersed in a bucket of water.			
Minimum radius of hot work to be two metres from other persons working. Screens should be erected if needed.			
Work areas to be kept **tidy** and free from combustible materials before and during the hot works. (Check both sides of partition walls in case heat can be transferred by conduction.)			
When working in **riser shafts** or on staging cylinders, work will be secured and openings to other levels covered with a fire blanket or other non-combustible materials.			
Operatives must remain in the area for 15 minutes **following completion** of work to ensure there is no hot spot residue.			

Operatives carrying out hot work	Yes	No	N/A
Must understand the permit conditions and the fire and safety precautions.			
Must be in possession of a permit at all times.			
Must stop work if required to do so by an authorised person.			
Must report immediately any hazard likely to affect the fire and safety precautions.			
Must ensure a satisfactory access/egress from the work area.			

Confirmation by contractor's supervisor: I confirm that the precautions specified above will be complied with and I will ensure that the persons carrying out the work, described above, are fully briefed on the safe method of work.

Name		**Position**		**Signature**		**Date**	

Confirmation by operator: I understand the precautions to be taken in carrying out the hot works.

Name		**Position**		**Signature**		**Date**	

Site management authorisation: I certify that the above work can commence with the precautions listed above.

Name		**Position**		**Signature**		**Date**	

Cancellation by operator: *(**Note:** hot works must cease one hour before end of shift.) I confirm that the work has been completed and the area has been checked and is safe.*

Name		**Position**		**Signature**		**Date**	

Cancellation by site management.

Name		**Position**		**Signature**		**Date**	

Inspection of area covered by hot-work permit by fire warden/site management after cancellation of permit	**Inspection completed after**		**1 hr**

Name		**Position**		**Signature**		**Date**	

GC

GC08 Electrical safety – Safe isolation checklist

Company name		Project title	
Location		Contract no.	

Overview

What you need to know

- ☑ Electricians and possibly some other trades will at times need to isolate electrical supplies so that electrical wiring systems and equipment can be installed, removed or otherwise worked upon.
- ☑ Not only the trades directly involved but others working nearby could be injured, burnt or killed if the isolation procedures go wrong.

What you need to do

- ☑ Make sure that an effective isolation procedure is in place and it is followed by the trades concerned.
- ☑ Make sure that the details of the isolation procedure have been communicated to all persons involved in operating it.

Significant hazards and risks

Safety	Yes	No	N/A
1. Is there a risk of electrocution and death?			
2. Is there a risk of impact injuries arising out of recoiling from contact with live electrical parts?			
Health	**Yes**	**No**	**N/A**
3. Is there a risk of electrical burns?			
4. Is there a risk of inhalation of smoke and other toxic fumes?			
Environment	**Yes**	**No**	**N/A**
5. Is there a risk of noxious fumes from the ignition of combustible materials?			
Managerial/supervisory tasks (including pre-planning)	**Yes**	**No**	**N/A**
6. Do contractors have a safe isolation procedure in place and have they explained it to you?			
7. Have you been informed each time prior to the safe isolation procedure being used?			
8. As far as possible, have checks been periodically made to ensure the procedure is being used properly?			
9. Have other trades been contacted, as necessary, when isolated circuits or equipment could adversely affect their safety?			
Training/competency requirements	**Yes**	**No**	**N/A**
10. Have training records been inspected to confirm that those involved in operating the safe isolation procedure are competent to do so?			
Safe systems of work/basic control measures	**Yes**	**No**	**N/A**
11. Is the safe isolation procedure itself at the heart of a safe system of work?			
12. Is the safe isolation procedure backed up with a permit to work system?			
Specific regulatory or special requirements	**Yes**	**No**	**N/A**
13. Management of Health and Safety at Work Regulations.			
14. Electricity at Work Regulations.			

GC08 Electrical safety – Safe isolation checklist *continued*

Further information
SELECT/HSE publication *Guidance on safe isolation procedures.*
HSE publication *Electrical safety and you, a brief guide* (INDG231).
HSE publication *Electricity at work: safe working practices* (HSG85).

Comments

Name		Position		Signature		Date	

GC09 Typical example of a permit to work

Company name		**Project title**	
Location		**Contract no.**	
Permit no.		**Site**	
Issued to		**Job**	

Treat all other electrical apparatus in the area as dangerous. The apparatus is efficiently connected to **earth** at the following points
The points of **isolation** are
Arrangements for the display or retention of the keys to locking-off devices are
Caution notices have been posted at the following points
Safety locks have been fitted at the following points
Description of the work to be carried out
Diagram of work/reference drawings
Sign off from authorised person. I hereby declare that the high-voltage apparatus in the area specified is dead, has been isolated from all live conductors and is connected to earth.

Name		**Position**		**Signature**		**Date**	

I hereby declare that I accept responsibility for carrying out work on the apparatus detailed on this permit to work and that no attempt will be made by me, nor by any person under my control, to carry out work on any other apparatus in the area.

Name		**Position**		**Signature**		**Date**	

Note: *after signature for work to proceed, this receipt must be signed by, and the permit to work retained by, the person in charge of the work, at the place where the work is being carried out, until work is suspended or completed and the clearance section has been signed.*

Clearance. The work for which this permit to work was issued is now suspended*/completed* and all people under my charge have been withdrawn and warned that it is no longer safe to work on the apparatus detailed on this permit to work. All work equipment, tools, test equipment, and so on have been removed. Additional earths have been removed.

The work is complete*/incomplete* as follows

Name		**Position**		**Signature**		**Date**	

The permit to work is hereby cancelled.

Name		**Position**		**Signature**		**Date**	

* Delete as applicable

GC10 PUWER inspection report

Provision and Use of Work Equipment Regulations (PUWER) inspection report

Company name		Project title	
Location		Contract no.	

Date and time of inspection	Description of plant or equipment	ID no.	Details of inspection *(defects identified and actions taken)*	Date of next inspection	Inspected by

GC11 Mobile plant examination – Periodic inspection and checks

Plant checked by operator/user. If defective, then quarantine and complete a plant defect report

Company name		Project title	
Location		Contract no.	

Date of inspection	Plant/equipment description and reference, including safe working load	Outcome of inspection *(if defective then remove from service and complete plant defect report)*	Name *(print)* and signature of person inspecting plant	Defect reported	Plant quarantined

GC

GC12 Construction plant reception and inspection report

Company name		**Project title**	
Location		**Contract no.**	
Equipment type and model		**Unique identification no.**	
Plant owner's name		**Plant user's name**	

	General	**Comments/actions**
1.	Is there any obvious visual damage (distressed welds) or missing parts?	
2.	Is the operator's manual provided securely with the item of plant?	
3.	Are items such as linkages, props, struts, cables and hoses in good order?	
4.	Does the plant clearly display all appropriate SWL, pressures or speeds?	
5.	Are all moving parts protected by fully operating and suitable guards?	
6.	Are suitable warning notices fitted where necessary?	
7.	Are all controls, including emergency stops, clearly identified and marked?	
8.	Is the plant generating excessive noise, fumes or other exhaust gases?	
9.	Are edge protection and handrails suitable and secure?	
10.	Are the brakes and steering fully functional?	
11.	Is the plant fitted with headlights, indicators, number plates and a horn?	
12.	Are the wheels/nuts, tyres or tracks intact and securely in place?	
13.	Is the plant fitted with working driver/passenger seating and restraints?	
14.	Is a falling object protective structure (FOPS) fitted where necessary?	
15.	Is a roll-over protective structure (ROPS) fitted?	
16.	Check fuel, engine/hydraulic oils and coolant levels, including leakage.	
17.	Is the item provided with secured special gas cylinders if LPG powered?	
18.	Is the item provided with the correct drawbar or tow hitch?	
19.	Other *(please state)*	
	Lifting equipment	**Comments/actions**
20.	Is the plant fitted with hydraulic check valves where necessary?	
21.	Are slewing or elevation restrictors fitted and working as necessary?	
22.	Are ancillary items (such as the chains, rope, hook and block) in good order?	
23.	Is the plant provided with sufficient working outriggers?	
24.	Is certificate of thorough examination in date (six or 12 months as appropriate)?	
25.	Is the automatic safe load indicator (ASLI) fitted and operational?	
26.	Other *(please state)*	
	Safety critical items	**Comments/actions**
27.	Does the operator have 360° visibility at a height and distance of one metre all around (this can be achieved by items immediately below)?	
28.	Is plant fitted with working reversing cameras or convex mirrors?	
29.	Is plant fitted with working reversing alarm, clearly audible at 10 metres?	
30.	Is the maximum gradient displayed or inclinometer provided where required?	
31.	Is plant fitted with a quick hitch/coupler?	
32.	Is plant fitted with amber beacon or light bar as necessary?	
33.	Does the plant have a suitable fire extinguisher in a convenient location?	
34.	Is plant fitted with fire or exhaust suppression systems for work in tunnels, etc?	

Comments

I have carried out the above checks where appropriate and have established to the best of my ability that this item is/is not* in safe working order *(*delete as applicable)*.

Name		**Position**		**Signature**		**Date**	

GC13 MEWP reception and inspection report

Company name		**Project title**	
Location		**Contract no.**	
Equipment type and model		**Unique identification no.**	
Plant owner's name		**Plant user's name**	

	General	**Comments/actions**
1.	Condition of the boom/scissor structure including pins, etc?	
2.	Is the operator's manual provided securely with the MEWP?	
3.	Are all boom operations fully functional?	
4.	Does the plant clearly display all appropriate SWL, etc?	
5.	Are all moving parts protected by fully operating and suitable guards?	
6.	Is the ground/basket switching of controls operating correctly?	
7.	Are all controls, including emergency stops, clearly identified and marked?	
8.	Is the plant generating excessive noise, fumes or other exhaust gases?	
9.	Are edge protection and handrails suitable and secure?	
10.	Are the brakes and steering fully functional?	
11.	Is the horn operating clearly?	
12.	Are the wheels/nuts, tyres or tracks intact and securely in place?	
13.	Are the directional travel instructions (decals) clearly identified on the body?	
14.	Is there a hand tool storage facility?	
15.	Condition of extending axles or outriggers, where fitted?	
16.	Check fuel, engine/hydraulic oils and coolant levels, including leakage.	
17.	Is the item provided with secured special gas cylinders if LPG powered?	
18.	Battery condition, including leads and where available water levels.	
19.	Are running and working lights functioning?	
20.	Hours run on receipt?	
21.	Other *(please state)*	
	Lifting equipment	**Comments/actions**
22.	Is certificate of thorough examination in date (six months)?	
23.	Are ancillary items (such as the chains, rope, and so on) in good order?	
24.	Other *(please state)*	
	Safety critical items	**Comments/actions**
25.	Does the plant have suitable attachment points for safety harnesses?	
26.	Are the dead-man's controls working correctly?	
27.	Is plant fitted with working travelling and tilt alarms, clearly audible at 10 metres?	
28.	Is the maximum gradient displayed or inclinometer provided where required?	
29.	Is the emergency lowering function enacted and operational?	
30.	Can a portable drain earth be attached when working in substations?	
31.	What is the maximum gradient for safe operation and is it displayed?	
32.	What is the maximum wind speed for safe operation and is it displayed?	
33.	Does the plant have a suitable fire extinguisher in a convenient location?	
34.	Is plant fitted with fire or exhaust suppression systems for work in tunnels, etc?	

Comments

I have carried out the above checks where appropriate and have established to the best of my ability that this item is/is not* in safe working order *(*delete as applicable)*.

Name		**Position**		**Signature**		**Date**	

GC

GC14 Lift plan

This lift plan is specific to the lifting operations described in the scope of works. It is not and should never be considered generic.

Company name		**Project title**	
Location		**Contract no.**	
Date of lifting operation			
Lift plan reference or activity			
Appointed person preparing this lift plan			
Date		**Signed**	
Lift supervisor			

Purpose

The purpose of this lifting plan is to identify the control measures necessary to negate the primary hazards of the:

- crane overturning
- load falling from the crane
- load or machine striking someone or any other identified hazard.

Scope of works

Details of crane provider

Company name			
Address			
Contact name		**Telephone**	

Details of crane operator(s)

CPCS card no. and operating history	

Load details *(also refer to lift schedule at end)*

Maximum weight		**Maximum size of load**	

Other details *(centre of gravity, lifting points, packaging, pallets and so on)*

GC

GC14 Lift plan *continued*

Details of crane			
Capacity and type			
Height *(ground – jib head)*		**Radius**	
Main jib length		**Fly jib length**	
Total jib length			
Safe working load		**Actual working load**	
Outrigger spread		**Counterbalance weight**	
Ground conditions *(CBR/Strata)*, **temporary works design in place and checked off** *(where appropriate)*			
Outrigger loadings			
Spread mat requirements			
Note: *where operating (jib) height equals or exceeds 10 m at any time, the appointed person must advise and consult with the manager from any airport/airfield within 6 km of the site.*			
Airport/airfield requirements			

Lifting accessories and configuration	
Equipment details	
Type *(for example spreader beam)*	
Safe working load *(**Note:** will configuration affect SWL?)*	

Sketch of slinging method

GC14 Lift plan *continued*

Site conditions and hazards

The following non-exhaustive list should be considered during the lift plan along with any other factors that could affect any aspect of the lift:

- excavations
- embankments
- overhead and underground services or obstructions
- culverts
- drainage
- manhole/inspection chambers
- buildings, stationary objects
- scaffolding
- plant and equipment
- roads
- rivers
- railways
- personnel and public
- other cranes
- environmental considerations.

Hazard	Control

Strength and stability

Ground conditions must be suitable and sufficient and remain so during crane lifts to take the anticipated loads. Include details of the ground conditions and any additional works required to the ground, including spreader mats specification and any testing regime required (for example, CBR tests).

A temporary works design must be in place and checked off before any lifting operation or crane set up takes place.

Weather/environmental considerations

Indicate in this section detail of wind speeds/environmental conditions that have been referenced/anticipated for the duration of the lifting operations.

Access

Include any special travelling routes, road closures/highways notifications, access problems.

Third party considerations

Over-sailing, works adjacent to railways, noise and restriction of view.

GC14 Lift plan *continued*

Emergency/breakdown procedures

Signalling
Indicate whether hand signals or radios are to be used. Also indicate signalling source and radio frequency/channel. This section can also include any unique slinger/signaller identification (that is, different colour helmet/hi-vis) if required.

Site and crane layout plan
Include crane position, lay-down/rigging area, position of delivery vehicles, landing points, banksman positions, ground and overhead hazards and exclusion zones. If required use elevation drawings.

GC14 Lift plan *continued*

Safe system of work – methodology
Include pre-lift, lift and post-lift.

Lift team
The details of this lift plan, along with any other associated risk assessment, method statement or safe system of work, have been brought to the attention of, and explained to, the persons listed below, who have acknowledged that they understand the contents, hazards and associated control measures.

Other relevant documentation *(list and attach)*

Name	Position	Signature	Date
	Site/project manager		
	Lift supervisor		
	Crane operator		
	Slinger/signaller		

This plan is specific to the lift as detailed in the scope of works.

In the event of any changes to circumstances, personnel or equipment, the plan should be reviewed and revised by the appointed person and any changes recommunicated to the lift team.

GC15 Lift schedule

Schedule of lifts (common lifts)

Company name		Project title	
Location		Contract no.	

Item to be lifted	Maximum weight	Crane used	Lifted from	Lifted to	Lifting accessories used	SWL	Comments

GC16 Site crane permit to lift (Part 1)

Company name		**Project title**	
Location		**Contract no.**	
Task/method statement no. (If applicable)			
Appointed person			
Employed by			
Date of visit		**Time of visit**	

Choose type of lift *(tick one lift only)*					
	Standard lift		Contract lift		Complex lift
Choose position *(tick one option below)*					
	Single crane position *(complete Part 1 only)*		Multiple crane positions *(complete Parts 1 and 2)*		
Description of works					

Load details			
Maximum weight		**Maximum size of load**	
Maximum radius		**Maximum lift height**	
Other *(e.g. unusual centre of gravity, lifting points, etc.)*			
Crane details			
Capacity and type			
Maximum available boom length		**Maximum boom length to be used for lift**	
Counterweight req.		**Hook block reeving** *(no. of falls)*	
Outrigger spread *(centre to centre)*	m. x m.	**Outrigger pad size** *(without mats)*	
Maximum outrigger load			
Site surface conditions			
Access for crane		**Access for transport**	
Lifting position		**Laydown area**	
Safe ground bearing capacity under outrigger		**Assessed by**	

Proximity hazards. (Provide details and attach sketch *(overhead lines, public roads, drains, ground conditions, etc.)*
A temporary works design for the lifting platform must be in place and signed off prior to setting up/commencing lifting operations. *(Permit Part 2 shall be completed for all crane positions/repositions of the crane.)*

GC16 Site crane permit to lift (Part 1) *continued*

Crane accessories required (state type and safe working load)			
Wire ropes		**Chains**	
Web slings		**Shackles**	
Beams		**Outrigger mats (state size)**	
Others (including specialist equipment)			
Operational requirements (such as road closures/possessions/site clearance)			
Permit valid from		**to**	

Crane team					
	Name	**CPCS card**		**Signature**	**Date**
		No.	**Expires**		
Appointed person					
Crane supervisors					
Crane operator					
Signaller/slinger					

Where contractors are required to complete this form, assistance shall be given by the site management authorised person who shall agree the details entered on the form and sign below.

Lifting operations must not commence until this form has been signed by the site management authorised person.

Name		**Position**		**Signature**		**Date**	

Distribution							
	Site file		Appointed person		Crane supervisor		Crane operator

If for any reason the details contained within this permit cannot be adhered to, the lifting operation must not continue and the appointed person must be notified immediately.

GC

GC17 Site crane permit to lift (Part 2)

Arrangements for multiple crane positions

I agree that the crane described in Part 1 may be re-positioned within the constraints defined within the lift plan, provided that each time it is set up in a new position the items in the list below are checked and signed for by the crane supervisor. When the crane is being operated by a contractor, each entry shall be countersigned by a site management person authorised by the project manager. The signature(s) shall be entered on this form prior to allowing the crane to operate in the new position.

Name		Position		Signature		Date	

This form shall remain in the crane cab during lifting operations and be returned to the site management project manager on completion of the lifting operations, as described in Part 1.

Position ref. as lift plan	Time	Date	Outriggers extended to spread stated in lift plan	All outriggers on crane platform and within designated lifting area defined in lift plan	Mats as defined in lift plan correctly placed under each outrigger	Additional items to be inserted by AP, if required		Crane lift supervisor's signature	Site management authorised signature

GC18 LOLER inspection report

The Lifting Operations and Lifting Equipment Regulations (LOLER) – Inspection report

Company name		Project title	
Location		Contract no.	

Lifting appliance and ID no.	Safe working load	Date of inspection	Time of inspection	Details identified that could give rise to a risk to the health or safety of any person	Can work be carried out safely?	If not, name of person informed

GC

GC18 LOLER inspection report *continued*

The Lifting Operations and Lifting Equipment Regulations (LOLER) – Inspection report

Company name		**Project title**	
Location		**Contract no.**	

Details of any action taken as a result of any matter identified *(details identified)*	**Details of any further action considered necessary**	**Name and particulars of the person making this report**	**Date of report**

GC19 Lifting equipment and accessories inspection report register

Company name					Project title				
Location					Contract no.				
Description of item	Date on site	ID no.	Safe working load	Owner	Date of last thorough examination	Date of next thorough exam	Date of last service	Date of next service	Date off site

GC

GD

High risk activities

The contents of this chapter should be read and used in conjunction with guidance contained within Section D.

Contents

GD01 Common access equipment checklist

Company name		**Project title**	
Location		**Contract no.**	

Common access equipment

Ladders	Yes	No	N/A
1. Is a ladder the right piece of access equipment to be using?			
2. Has the person received training in the correct use of the equipment?			
3. Are ladders only used for very light work of short duration or access?			
4. Are all ladders properly stored and inspected regularly?			
5. Are the ladders that are being used suited to the purpose or use to which they are being put?			
6. Are there any damaged, loose or missing parts?			
7. Are the rungs of ladders clean and free of mud or grease?			
8. Are sufficient persons available to handle and place ladders properly and safely?			
9. Are ladders set on firm and level ground?			
10. Are ladders properly erected and secured?			
11. If there is not an alternative suitable handhold, does the ladder project sufficiently above the landing place?			
12. Is the overlap correct on extension ladders?			
13. Are the methods for raising tools or materials safe?			
14. Are ladders placed so that the work does not involve overreaching?			
15. Is suitable footwear that will give a satisfactory grip and prevent slipping being worn?			
16. Are ladders set at the correct angle of 75°?			
17. Are ladders clear of excavations or other potential hazards?			
18. Are ladders being leant against or secured to any fragile material?			
19. Are all lashings used of sound material and made properly secure?			
Stepladders	**Yes**	**No**	**N/A**
20. Has the person received training in the correct use of the equipment?			
21. Is the stepladder level and stable?			
22. Is it open to the full extent of the retaining cords or hinges?			
23. Are steps set at right angles to the workface wherever possible?			
24. Are the user's knees below the top step?			
25. Could the person using the stepladder fall a distance that would cause an injury?			
26. Is the person using the ladder not using the top third?			
Trestles	**Yes**	**No**	**N/A**
27. Are trestles, and any boards that are being used with the trestles, safe, undamaged and of adequate strength?			
28. Has the person received training in the correct use of the equipment?			
29. Are the trestles set on a firm and level base?			
30. Is the working platform of a sufficient width for the job in hand?			
31. Are guard-rails and toe-boards fitted to trestle platforms, if indicated as being necessary by a risk assessment?			
32. Where indicated as necessary by a risk assessment, is the trestle tied to the adjacent structure?			

GD01 Common access equipment checklist *continued*

Trestles *continued*	**Yes**	**No**	**N/A**
33. Is a safe ladder access provided?			
34. Is the maximum permitted distributed load indicated and complied with?			
Podium steps	**Yes**	**No**	**N/A**
35. Are the podium steps of sufficient size and the correct type for the task?			
36. Has the person received training in the correct use of the equipment?			
37. Have the operators been supplied with and fully understand the supplier's instructions for use?			
38. Are all of the components available and in good condition?			
39. Is the floor surface sound and of a level construction?			
40. Are brakes provided, in working order and used?			
41. Do all podium steps carry unique identifying marks and are they subjected to frequent inspection?			
Management responsibilities	**Yes**	**No**	**N/A**
42. Are the regulations and guidance on work at height that is appropriate to ladders, stepladders, podium steps, trestles and other access equipment known and have management received training in the correct application of the equipment?			
43. Has any safer system of work or access been considered?			
44. Do management know how and where access equipment is being used by employees?			
45. Have permanently fixed ladders been installed wherever possible?			
46. Has any necessary safety equipment been provided?			
47. Has adequate storage for ladders and access equipment been provided?			
48. Has a system of proper inspection and the keeping of records for all ladders and access equipment been implemented?			
49. Are all ladders, stepladders, podium steps, trestles and boards of sound design and manufacture, and kept in good condition?			
50. Have all users been properly instructed and trained, and are competent to use the equipment safely and without risk to themselves or others?			
51. Is proper supervision of **all** employees who are using any form of access equipment provided?			

Comments

Name		**Position**		**Signature**		**Date**	

GD02 Scaffold planning and work at height activities checklist

Company name		**Project title**	
Location		**Contract no.**	

Design stage

Element	Yes	No	N/A	Comments
Considerations at design stage				
Have discussions taken place with scaffold designers?				
Has the building design considered work at height issues?				
How will the building be maintained? Are the high-level services (such as lighting) easy to get to?				
Will ground conditions be suitable for the scaffold and supporting elements?				
Will steel sections allow fixing of load-bearing scaffold components?				
Will site access suit heavy vehicle deliveries?				
If a high-rise project, have climbing screens been considered in the floor slab designs?				
If a fully-glazed building, is an external scaffold required and can it be fixed to the façade?				
What scaffold standard will be required? (TG20, BS EN 12811)				

Tender stage

Element	Yes	No	N/A	Comments
Provisional design				
Procedure for ensuring only final design used				
Quotations – scaffolding tender stage				
Criteria required from sub-contractors to be invited to tender (see scaffold specification template)				
Membership of key trade association:				
■ NASC				
■ FASET				
Industry standard safety record				
Previous experience of this application				
Resources (no. employees/assets)				
Qualifications of workforce				
Good safety management system				
Financial stability				
Access to designers				

GD

GD02 Scaffold planning and work at height activities checklist *continued*

Scaffold design

Element	Yes	No	N/A	Comments
Is a scaffold design needed?				
Is it a standard configuration? *(refer to Work at Height Regulations)*				
Is it designed to TG20 or equivalent?				
Is it a basic scaffold, to TG20?				
Does BS EN 12811 apply instead?				
Is it a system scaffold?				
Does it meet the manufacturer's data sheets standard configuration?				
Have you seen the manufacturer's data sheets?				
Has the latest wind code been applied?				
Eurocode 1 (BS EN 1991-1-4:2005)				
Third party/in house temporary works checking scaffold design?				
Means of access?				
What type of access to working levels? *(see NASC hierarchy)* (NASC *Access and egress from scaffolds* (SG25)				
What is the height to top working area?				
What is the duration of project requiring access?				
How many people using it?				
Preference: staircase				
Otherwise: internal or external ladders				
Any edge protection details where BS EN 13374 applies?				
Has scaffold design drawing been received?				
Are tie loadings and positions shown?				
Is rating for scaffold load class shown?				
Are loading bays designed?				
Are loading bay gates included?				

Anchorage systems/scaffold ties

Element	Yes	No	N/A	Comments
Method anchoring/securing				
Types of ties to be used:				
NASC Anchorage systems for scaffolding (TG4)				
Ring (Hilti). Concrete, not brickwork				
Screwplug. Concrete and suitable brickwork				
Chemical anchors. Concrete and suitable brickwork				
Self-tapping (excalibur). Concrete and suitable brickwork				
Through ties				
Reveal ties. Max 50%				
Rakers and butt ties				
If buttress to be used...design requested				

GD

GD02 Scaffold planning and work at height activities checklist *continued*

Anchorage systems/scaffold ties *continued*

Element	Yes	No	N/A	Comments
Tie testing				
Confirm requirements for testing reports				
Minimum of 5% to be tested *(see* TG4 *11)*				
Regular calibration of tie test equipment				
*Timber-frame construction				

Contract awarded

Element	Yes	No	N/A	Comments
Scaffold sub-contractor appointed – Scaffold details				
Procedure to ensure final drawing is issued to replace provisional				
Review scaffold design *(confirm to* TG20 *or manufacturer's design data)*				
If system scaffold, check manufacture source (NASC *System scaffold Code of Practice*)				
Internal edge protection details (NASC SG29)				
Need for securing of scaffold boards? Criteria stated? *(Tying down of scaffold boards* (TG12))				

Specify permitted gaps	
Internal service gap	mm
Between main and inside platform	mm
Between boards/decking	mm
Gaps in guard-rail/edge protection	mm

Confirm start date		**Programme timings**	

Delivery of scaffold materials

Element	Yes	No	N/A	Comments
How will it be delivered and unloaded?				
Unloading (*Working from vehicles* (SG30))				
Banksman *(check qualification)*				
Unloading safety work at height methods:				
▪ site gantry/alsipercha				
▪ entirely crane/forklift handled				
▪ truck with edge protection/netting				
▪ personal fall arrest				
Lifting (NASC *Use, inspection and maintenance of lifting equipment and accessories for lifting in scaffolding* (SG9))				

GD02 Scaffold planning and work at height activities checklist *continued*

Erection process				
Element	**Yes**	**No**	**N/A**	**Comments**
Who will build it?				
Qualifications of scaffolders				
Confirm requirement of qualifications of scaffolders *(ratio of advanced/scaffolder/trainee)*				
Traditional scaffolding qualification (CISRS *Part 1 Scaffolder*)				
System scaffold (*should be type specific*) (CISRS *System scaffold training*)				
Mobile aluminium/GRP towers (PASMA)				
Erectors and installers competency *(scaffolder CISRS card qualifications)*				
Cards seen:				
■ Labourer				
■ Trainee				
■ Scaffolder				
■ Advanced scaffolder				
Alternatives				
MEWPs (IPAF)				
Mobile towers (PASMA)				
How will it be built?				
Erection system of work. (CISRS Scaffolder (SG4))				
Erection system of work. (PASMA Mobile towers. 3T/Advanced guard-rail system)				
SG4 *Toolbox talk training confirmation*				
Inspection of fall protection/fall-arrest equipment (NASC SG16 and SG17 *Management of fall protection equipment*)				
Evidence of working to SG4? (single guard-rail clearly visible on scaffolds)				
Safe system of work (NASC *Guide to risk assessments* (SG27))				
Site specific risk assessment				
Method statements				
Pre-start risk assessment				
Rescue plan				
Method statement				
Rescue plan (NASC *Guide to formulating a rescue plan* (SG19))				
Evidence of training				
Confirm plan not reliant on emergency services				

GD

GD02 Scaffold planning and work at height activities checklist *continued*

Inspection regime				
Element	**Yes**	**No**	**N/A**	**Comments**
Inspection, qualifications and signing of scaffolding register.				
Sub-contractor *(Advanced scaffolder or* CISRS *two-day scaffold inspection certificate?)*				
Independent safety consultant				
Own staff (CISRS *Two-day scaffold inspection certificate?*)				
More complex designed structures. (CISRS *Advanced scaffold inspection course?*)				
Retain record for three months				
Inspection of safety nets				
Who is inspecting nets? (FASET *management/inspection course*)				
Scafftag system to be used?				
PASMA tag system for mobile towers?				
Completion of scaffold				
Scaffold handover certificate (NASC *Handover of scaffold structures* (SG35))				

Other matters				
Element	**Yes**	**No**	**N/A**	**Comments**
Ongoing work at height control				
Scaffolders wearing harnesses?				
Regularly clipping on when required?				
Is scaffold being altered by non-scaffolders? (NASC *Unauthorised modification of scaffolds* (SG36))				
Safety nets (*Safety nets* (SG14))				
Installed by FASET qualified persons?				
Specification of netting? *(BS EN 1263-2)*				
Storage on site arrangements made?				
Requirements for particular structures				
Steelwork				
Scaffolders accessing steelwork? (NASC 27 *Temporary edge protection on open steelwork*)				
Timber frame (NASC *Safe system of work for scaffolding associated with timber-frame building construction* (SG28))				
House building (NASC *Requirements for use of brickguards* (SG10))				
Temporary roofs (NASC *Guide to the design and construction of temporary roofs and buildings* (TG9))				
Traditional tube and fittings temporary roof				
System-type temporary roof				

GD

GD02 Scaffold planning and work at height activities checklist *continued*

Element	Yes	No	N/A	Comments
Materials compliance (NASC *Guide to risk assessments* (SG27))				
Equipment				
Tube *(BS EN 39:2001)*				
Fittings *(BS EN 74 and* TG17 *Identification of EN 74 fittings)*				
Scaffold boards *(BS 2482 1.2 m and 1.5 m span)*				
System scaffold *(BS EN 12810)*				
MEWPs				
Mobile towers *(BS EN 1004)*				
Podium steps *(draft PASMA document)*				
Edge protection *(system or tube and fittings) (BS EN 13374)*				
Ground conditions preparation				
Has the ground been prepared?				
Any heavy imposed loads?				
Scaffold *(soft and medium hard ground)*				
Mobile elevating platform *(hard surface (such as concrete, tarmac))*				
Mobile access tower *(hard surface (such as concrete, tarmac))*				

Comments							
Name		**Position**		**Signature**		**Date**	

(Thanks to National Access and Scaffolding Confederation and AIF for their help in producing this checklist.)

GD

GD03 Inspection checklist

Check at each inspection that the scaffold does not have these faults.

Footings	1	2	3	4
Soft and uneven				
No base plates				
No sole boards				
Undermined				

Bracing (facade and ledger)	1	2	3	4
Some missing				
Loose				
Wrong fittings				

Ties	1	2	3	4
Some missing				
Loose				

Standards	1	2	3	4
Not plumb				
Jointed at same height				
Wrong spacing				
Damaged				

Putlogs and transoms	1	2	3	4
Loose				
Wrongly spaced				
Wrongly supported				

Boarding	1	2	3	4
Bad boards				
Trap boards				
Incomplete boarding				
Insufficient supports				

Ledgers	1	2	3	4
Loose				
Not level				
Joint in same bays				
Damaged				

Couplings	1	2	3	4
Wrong fitting				
No check couplers				
Loose				
Damaged				

Guard-rails and toe-boards	1	2	3	4
Loose				
Wrong height				
Some missing				

Bridles	1	2	3	4
Weak support				
Wrong spacing				
Wrong couplings				

Ladders	1	2	3	4
Not tied				
Damaged				
Insufficient length				

Key: 1 = good, 2 = average, 3 = poor, 4 = N/A

GD04 Handover certificate

This is a type of handover certificate that could be used. Employers could also consider a form of handover certificate that meets the requirements of the Work at Height Regulations schedule for the inspection requirement before first use.

Company name		**Project title**	
Location		**Contract no.**	
Scaffolding – handing over certificate			
To *(contractor)*			
Date		**Time**	
Description of scaffold or section of scaffold handed over			
Drawing no. *(where applicable)*			

Scaffolding, as described above, has now been completed and complies with the Work at Height Regulations and current standards. It is structurally sound and should only be used and loaded in accordance with our quotation number:				
Use only for				
Loading to be		**working lifts with distributed load of**		**(kN/M² lbs/ft² per lift)**

The detailed requirements of the regulations with regard to guard-rails, working platforms, toe-boards, bracing and ties have been complied with.

In order to comply with the regulations, this scaffold must be inspected before being taken into use for the first time, at regular intervals not exceeding seven days since the last inspection, after any event likely to have jeopardised the safety of the scaffold and after any substantial addition, dismantling or other alteration. Particulars of each inspection must be recorded in a report of inspection.

This scaffold has/has not *(delete as appropriate)* been designed to take tarpaulin sheets (or other windsails).

Scaffold contractor							
Name		**Position**		**Signature**		**Date**	
Certificate received on behalf of the contractor							
Name		**Position**		**Signature**		**Date**	

GD05 Scaffold inspection report

Scaffold inspection report (in line with the Work at Height Regulations)

Company name			Project title		
Location			Contract no.		

No.	Location and description of workplace inspected	Date and time of inspection	Matters observed that give rise to any health and safety risks	Details of action taken at time of inspection	Details of any further action considered necessary	Name, signature and position of inspector

GD

GD06 Boatswain's chair (bosun's chair) checklist

Company name		Project title	
Location		Contract no.	

Boatswain's chair (bosun's chair)

Before use	Yes	No	N/A
1. Has a risk assessment been carried out?			
2. Have emergency rescue procedures been established?			
3. Has a separately anchored safety line been installed?			
4. Is the installation and use of a boatswain's chair supervised by trained, experienced and competent personnel?			
5. Is the chair and associated equipment carefully examined for defects prior to use?			
6. Is confirmation at hand that test and examination certificates are valid?			
7. Has the safe working load been established?			
8. Have checks been carried out to ensure that the user is both trained and competent in the use of the chair?			
9. Are warning notices displayed and has notification of intention to carry out work been given?			
During use	**Yes**	**No**	**N/A**
10. Is the chair free of materials or articles that could interfere with the user's control of the chair?			
11. Has the fall rope been properly tied off whilst the chair is in use and always under or around a cleat to act as a brake?			
12. Has a safe area been created below the work area or protection installed?			
13. Is the safety line being properly used?			
After use	**Yes**	**No**	**N/A**
14. Is the chair inspected for defects following its use?			
15. Are chairs and ropes left in a safe condition, in other words:			
a) is the chair raised to the first floor level if possible, and the top rope secured?			
b) have the chair and rope been secured to prevent swing?			
c) have the ropes (and chair, if timber) been dried before storage?			

Comments

Name		Position		Signature		Date	

GD07 Access cradles checklist

Company name		Project title	
Location		Contract no.	

Cradles

Before use	Yes	No	N/A
1. Has a risk assessment been carried out?			
2. Have emergency rescue procedures been established?			
3. Are cradles installed and supervised by a competent person?			
4. Are cradles inspected and appropriate reports made?			
5. Are current test certificates available for winches, wire ropes, blocks and so on?			
6. Have users been properly trained?			
7. Has adequate protection been installed and proper warning given to members of the public and other people who might be affected?			
8. Have occupiers of the building been warned not to open windows?			
9. Have steps been taken to erect the correct warning signs?			
10. Have secondary safety ropes and harnesses been provided as necessary?			
11. Is the safe working load of the cradle marked?			
12. Has a check been carried out for obstructions on the face of the structure?			
13. Have effective fall-arrest measures been installed?			
During use	**Yes**	**No**	**N/A**
14. Is a competent person in charge of all operations when cradles are being used?			
15. Are operations being carried out with authorised operatives only?			
16. Are inspections carried out weekly?			
17. Have checks been made to ensure that there are no knots or kinks in the ropes?			
18. Are ropes correctly reeved on the drum with at least two turns left when the cradle has reached its maximum operating distance? (Power-operated cradles only.)			
19. Have both power supplies and cables been checked before operating?			
20. Have checks been carried out to the controls for correct function and to ensure that pendant controls are secured to the cradle?			
21. Have all ropes been securely anchored?			
22. Are the stops and over-runs operational?			
23. Are secondary safety devices properly secured and anchored?			
24. Has the cradle been tied-off to the building to prevent sway?			
25. Have checks been made to ensure that the safe working load is not being exceeded?			
26. Is the cradle kept clean and clear of rubbish?			
27. Have all necessary precautions been taken to ensure that the platform is not slippery?			
28. Are all tools carried in the cradle secure?			
29. Is there adequate protection from above to stop any falling materials?			
30. Are all necessary steps being taken to ensure that the proper access is being used?			
31. Is the practice of climbing down ropes strictly prohibited?			
32. Are all personnel aware that there must be no transferring between adjacent cradles?			
33. Have all possible steps been taken to ensure that personnel do not allow ropes and cradles or connections to lie in gutters?			

GD07 Access cradles checklist *continued*

During use *continued*	Yes	No	N/A
34. Are all operatives aware that use in high winds or adverse weather conditions is not safe and is prohibited?			
After use	**Yes**	**No**	**N/A**
35. Are the cradle and all ropes in a secure position to prevent unauthorised access or usage?			
36. Are checks carried out to ensure that power supplies are isolated and control equipment is removed and secured?			
37. Are defects and breakdowns reported promptly and correctly?			
38. Are all warning signs removed after the completion of work?			
Management information	**Yes**	**No**	**N/A**
39. Has it been established that the supplier is reputable and experienced?			
40. Has the necessary communication taken place between the user and supplier?			
41. Do both parties have the necessary competence?			
42. Have other parties been consulted as necessary?			

Comments

Name		Position		Signature		Date	

GD08 Safety belts, harnesses and lanyards checklist

Company name		Project title	
Location		Contract no.	

Safety belts, harnesses and lanyards			
Before use	**Yes**	**No**	**N/A**
1. Has a risk assessment been carried out?			
2. Have emergency rescue procedures been established?			
3. Has the most suitable harness or belt been selected for the type of operation and hazard?			
4. Are the operatives who are to use the equipment adequately trained in its inspection and use?			
5. Is it all in good order and fit for purpose?			
6. Is a secure and appropriately positioned anchorage point available?			
7. Have checks been made to ensure that the weather conditions are such that an operative can work safely in the prevailing conditions?			
8. Is there a schedule of detailed examination of the equipment?			
9. Are records of the examinations kept?			
10. Have steps been taken to see that adequate warning notices are displayed?			
During use	**Yes**	**No**	**N/A**
11. Have safety lines been set by a competent person?			
12. Are only authorised, trained and competent personnel allowed to use the equipment?			
13. Is all equipment inspected before the start of work each day, following an established routine, particularly for damage to webbing lanyards?			
14. Have set procedures been established and implemented?			
15. Is messing about strictly prohibited?			
After use	**Yes**	**No**	**N/A**
16. Is the equipment inspected for damage?			
17. Are defects reported promptly and correctly?			
18. Is defective equipment quarantined (if it can be repaired) or discarded?			
19. Is the equipment cleaned and stored correctly?			

Comments							
Name		Position		Signature		Date	

GD

GD09 Safety nets checklist

Company name		Project title	
Location		Contract no.	

Safety nets

Before use	Yes	No	N/A
1. Has a risk assessment been carried out?			
2. Are the safety nets rigged to minimise the height of any fall such that an uninjured person can simply climb out?			
3. If not, have emergency rescue procedures been established?			
4. Have checks been made to ensure that freefall distances are not more than specified?			
5. Have safety nets been rigged by trained and competent persons?			
6. Is the use of safety nets to be supervised by competent persons?			
7. Have safety nets been inspected prior to current use?			
8. Are complete and proper records kept of all inspections and examinations?			
9. Has the safety net system been inspected within the previous week?			
10. Are all anchors and supports secure?			
11. Is the safety net clear of all debris?			
12. Have checks been made to ensure that nothing is positioned under the net to reduce the minimum clearance distance required?			
During use	**Yes**	**No**	**N/A**
13. Is the net being kept clear of debris?			
14. Are the safety nets inspected:			
a) after a fall			
b) for the effects of contamination			
c) every seven days during use to ensure that the safety net is not damaged and that the anchorage points and ties are sound?			
After use	**Yes**	**No**	**N/A**
15. Are safety nets inspected for any damage following use and before being stowed away?			
16. Are any defects reported promptly and correctly?			
17. Are repairs only carried out by a competent person?			
18. Are adequate records maintained as to the use and condition of safety nets?			
19. Are safety nets dried and stored correctly?			
20. Are the annual condition tests being undertaken?			

Comments

Name		Position		Signature		Date	

GD

GD10 Steelwork erection checklist

Company name		**Project title**	
Location		**Contract no.**	

Steelwork

	Yes	No	N/A
1. Is the contractor responsible for erection competent?			
2. Has a risk assessment been undertaken for the project?			
3. Does the contractor have a method statement?			
4. Does it specify the sequence of erection and how the structure will be kept stable at all times?			
5. Does everyone know what types of temporary support will be used?			
6. Does everyone know the requirements for safe erection?			
7. Does everyone know how the structure components will be erected and connected safely?			
8. Will as many connections as possible be done at ground level?			
9. Where work must be done at height, have safe means of access and safe places of work been planned?			
10. Has the site been surveyed for hazardous features (such as overhead power lines)?			
11. Is there sufficient access for off-loading lorries?			
12. Is there a planned delivery sequence of components?			
13. Are there plans to deal with lorries that have to reverse?			
14. How will components be off-loaded, stacked and de-stacked safely?			
15. Are the weights of individual components known?			
16. Does all lifting gear that is to be used have adequate safe working loads?			
17. Have crane capacities been calculated?			
18. Have steps been taken to eliminate the need for manual handling?			
19. Are the steel erectors competent? Have they been adequately trained?			
20. Will all lifts be supervised by a competent person?			
21. If MEWPs are to be used, are all the operators trained and competent?			
22. Is it necessary to survey and prepare the ground so that MEWPs can operate safely?			
23. Will work at height be carried out other than from a MEWP?			
24. Does everyone know what measures will be taken to prevent or arrest falls?			
25. Are emergency rescue procedures in place?			
26. Have any special risks been identified (for example, work in confined spaces)?			
27. Is there a plan to monitor the weather?			
28. Is there a contingency plan?			

Comments

Name		**Position**		**Signature**		**Date**	

GD

GD11 Excavations checklist

Company name		**Project title**	
Location		**Contract no.**	

Overview

What you need to know

When preparing for an excavation there are many factors to take into consideration. The checklist below will identify the significant hazards and risks to be considered. These will include soil composition, depth, support structures and emergency evacuation.

What you need to do

Refer to information detailed in the health and safety plan, which should identify hazards that may impact on your excavation (such as underground services and adjacent buildings). Ensure the design takes account of traffic routes, material storage and lay-down areas, and the proximity of external factors (such as neighbouring businesses, public roads and spaces).

Significant hazards and risks

Safety	**Yes**	**No**	**N/A**
1. Is there a design for the excavation and have identified hazards been taken into account (such as traffic routes and location within the site)?			
2. Is temporary lighting provided for periods of darkness or foggy conditions?			
3. Has a risk assessment of the task been prepared, covering risks from hazards identified and showing control measures to be implemented?			
4. Has an emergency plan been provided showing how workers will be removed from the excavation (such as during a medical emergency or accident)?			
Health	**Yes**	**No**	**N/A**
5. Have the workers been issued with additional appropriate PPE and RPE?			
6. Has the excavation been purged of any gases prior to being entered by workers?			
7. Are there any hazardous substances being used – COSHH?			
8. Has soil sampling been carried out to check for contaminants?			
Environment	**Yes**	**No**	**N/A**
9. Has the site been designed so that the excavation is not at risk from vehicle and plant movement around the site (such as surcharging the walls of the trench)?			
10. Have surveys been undertaken to check for underground services that could be affected or damaged by the excavation (such as cable exposed by installation of a trench box)?			
11. Are there neighbouring structures or features that would affect the integrity of the excavation (such as watercourses, roads and railway lines)? Archaeology also needs to be considered.			
Managerial/supervisory tasks (including pre-planning)	**Yes**	**No**	**N/A**
12. Have the risk assessments been prepared and approved for excavation work to commence and include emergency rescue information, and access and egress?			
13. Has a traffic management plan been prepared showing site(s) for excavation(s)?			
14. Have welfare facilities been arranged for the site – suitable for tasks and number of workers anticipated (showers, drying facilities and lockers for storage of clothing)?			
15. Have workers got adequate PPE and any additional equipment made available (such as overalls, RPE and goggles)?			
16. Have arrangements been made for inspections of the excavation as required by legislation?			

GD11 Excavations checklist *continued*

Training/competency requirements	Yes	No	N/A
17. Do the workers have the requisite skills for the tasks to be undertaken (are they competent, do they have confined space training)?			
18. Are CPCS/CSCS and/or alternative qualification cards required for the project?			
19. How frequently will safety inspections take place?			
20. Have the operatives been trained in the use of RPE that may be required (such as face fitting of the mask)?			
Safe systems of work and basic control measures	**Yes**	**No**	**N/A**
21. Have method statements and risk assessments been approved prior to contractors commencing on site?			
22. Have workers been briefed on the methodology, hazards and risks and do they understand the control measures required?			
23. Have checks been carried out to prove any unsupported ground is safe?			
24. Do excavations have adequate support and shoring or are they benched or battered to prevent possible collapse?			
25. Where risk of flooding exists, have cofferdams or caissons been installed with pumps?			
26. Have suitable barriers been erected around excavations to prevent materials, plant, people or excavation operatives falling in (such as fencing, guard-rails and toe-boards)?			
27. Are poorly ventilated areas continually monitored for the presence of gas?			
28. Have stop barriers been used to prevent vehicle entry?			
29. Are spoil and materials stacked at least 1.5 m from the edge of the excavation?			
30. Are ladders provided for safe access and egress?			
31. Have cable location devices (CAT and Genny) and utility drawings been used to trace underground services prior to commencement of work?			
32. Have suitable signs and barriers been provided to warn of the work?			
33. Have water discharges off site been approved by the Environmental Agency or Local Authority?			
34. Where possible, has permission and discharge to the foul sewer been gained?			
35. If discharging into watercourses or soakaways, an advanced discharge licence and suitable treatment will be required that could involve the use of a settlement lagoon, tank or grassed area. Has this been gained?			
36. Has site run-off been prevented from entering watercourses or surface water drainage and, where possible, water prevented from entering excavations?			
Specific regulatory or special requirements	**Yes**	**No**	**N/A**
37. Are there registers on site for statutory excavation inspection?			
38. Has an emergency plan for evacuation from the excavation been prepared and communicated to the workers on site and in the excavation?			
39. Does the excavation need a permit to work (such as confined space or underground services)?			

Further information

- ☑ The Construction (Design and Management) Regulations.
- ☑ HSE publication *Avoiding danger from underground services* (HSG47).
- ☑ HSE publication *The safe use of vehicles on construction sites* (HSG144).
- ☑ HSE publication *The Confined Spaces Regulations, Approved Code of Practice, regulations and guidance* (L101).

Comments

Name		Position		Signature		Date	

GD12 Permit to dig

Work must not start until Sections A, B and C of this permit have been completed and signed by authorised persons.

Company name		**Project title**	
Location		**Contract no.**	

Section A. Project details (To be completed by project or package manager)			
Contractor			
Date and time issued		**Completion date**	
Supervisor in charge of works *(print name)*		**Operatives** *(print name)*	
Brief description of works			

Section B. Precautions to be taken before work is carried out (To be completed by the supervisor in charge of the works)

Essential procedures	Yes	No	Comments
1. Contract drawings and details issued by the client or otherwise obtained.			
2. Drawings show the location, type and status of underground services.			
3. Live services made dead as far as it is possible or necessary to do so.			
4. Work area surveyed by a competent person, using appropriate detection equipment to confirm the exact location of underground services.			
5. Location of services marked on the ground.			
6. Valid method statement and risk assessment in place.			
7. Method statement and risk assessment explained to the operatives carrying out the work.			
8. Person in charge of the excavation is fully conversant with the principles of safe digging and/or avoidance of underground services.			
9. All operatives familiar with safe excavation practices.			
10. If plant is being used, operator is competent and familiar with safe digging practices.			
11. State type, serial number and calibration test date of cable avoidance equipment used.			

Confirmation by contractor's supervisor: I confirm that the precautions specified above will be complied with and I will ensure that the persons carrying out the work, described above, are fully briefed on the safe method of work.

Name		**Position**		**Signature**		**Date**	

Confirmation by operator(s): I understand the precautions to be taken in carrying out the works.

Name		**Position**		**Signature**		**Date**	

GD

GD12 Permit to dig *continued*

Section C. Completion of work
(To be completed by the supervisor in charge of the works)

I am satisfied that:

- the excavation has been backfilled and the surface reinstated*
- the work is completed and the area has been left in a safe condition*
- the work area is clear of operatives and all equipment*
- utility company(ies) have been informed that services made dead may now be reactivated*

I am **not** satisfied that the work has been completed satisfactorily and the additional work described below must be completed before this permit may be cancelled*.

** Delete as appropriate*

Name		Position		Signature		Date	

Additional work that is necessary to enable this permit to be cancelled.

Section D. Cancellation of permit
(To be completed by the supervisor in charge of the works)

I am satisfied that all work has been completed and this permit is now cancelled.

Name		Position		Signature		Date	

GD13 Excavation inspection report

Report of inspection on excavations/cofferdams/caissons*

* Delete as appropriate

The Construction (Design and Management) Regulations, Regulations 22, 23 and 24

Company name		Project title	
Location		Contract no.	
Address of site			
Inspection carried out on behalf of			
Inspection carried out by		Position	

Date and time of inspection	Location inspected	Description of place of work, or part inspected	Details of any matter identified giving rise to a risk to the health and safety of any person	Details of any action taken as a result of any matter identified	Details of any further action considered necessary

GD

GD14 Work on high voltage equipment permit

Company name		**Project title**	
Location		**Contract no.**	
Issued to		**Job**	

I hereby declare that it is safe to work on the following high voltage apparatus, which is dead, isolated from all live conductors and is connected to earth.

Name		**Position**		**Signature**		**Date**	

All other apparatus is dangerous

Switching and isolating. The apparatus is disconnected from all live conductors by the following operations

Earthing. The equipment is earthed at the following points

Danger notices are posted at

Automatic fire extinguishing control has been rendered inoperative at

Other precautions

Sign off from authorised person.

Name		**Position**		**Signature**		**Date**	

I hereby declare that I accept responsibility for carrying out work on the apparatus detailed on this permit and that no attempt will be made by me, nor by any person under my control, to carry out work on any other apparatus.

Name		**Position**		**Signature**		**Date**	

***Note**: after signature for work to proceed, this receipt must be signed by, and the permit to work retained by, the person in charge of the work until work is suspended or completed and the clearance section has been signed.*

This is to certify that the work authorised above has been completed or stopped and that all workers under my charge have been withdrawn and warned that it is no longer safe to work on the apparatus specified on this permit to work and that gear, tools and additional earthing connections are all cleared. Automatic fire extinguishing control has been restored.

Permit to work is hereby cancelled by the authorised person.

Name		**Position**		**Signature**		**Date**	

GD

GD15 Underground and overhead services checklist

Company name		Project title	
Location		Contract no.	

Overview
What you need to know
When you plan to undertake works that may cross above underground services or below overhead services there are many hazards that need to be taken into consideration. With both types of services the risks are potentially fatal and can also have large scale serious consequences and costs (such as power outage to an area, including hospitals and businesses).
What you need to do
Plans and drawings provided with the health and safety construction phase plan should detail existing underground and overhead services to provide a starting point. These can never be guaranteed to be accurate, so you will need to make contact with all local utility companies and then carry out appropriate investigations. Following that, a safe system of work can be devised, in conjunction with all relevant parties.

Significant hazards and risks			
Safety	**Yes**	**No**	**N/A**
1. Have all previous plans and drawings been obtained for the site?			
2. Have all the utility companies been contacted for information, including any private ones, before any work commences on site (such as telecommunications)?			
3. Have risk assessments and method statements been reviewed prior to any investigations being done?			
4. Ensure that all necessary investigations are undertaken before any works are commenced, including site set up and any ground works (such as CAT and Genny).			
Health	**Yes**	**No**	**N/A**
5. Prior to works starting near overhead services, have suitable barriers and goal posts been erected, and signage put in place indicating safe passage, where necessary?			
6. Have all workers been informed of the dangers of working with either underground or overhead services (such as injuries from electrical contact or fire or explosion from gas mains)?			
7. Have suitable welfare facilities been provided – as in CDM Schedule 2?			
8. Have an adequate number of suitably trained first aiders been provided, given the increased severity of risk from this type of work?			
Environment	**Yes**	**No**	**N/A**
9. Has the site been designed to either eliminate or reduce risks from overhead services (such as when preparing the traffic management plan)?			
10. Have surveys been undertaken to check for underground services that could be affected or damaged by excavation, by vehicles and plant crossing them, and so on?			
Managerial/supervisory tasks (including pre-planning)	**Yes**	**No**	**N/A**
11. Has the construction phase plan been approved and does it include information on overhead and underground services?			
12. Have you or the project manager set up communication links with the utility services?			
13. Have the necessary inspections and/or investigations been completed and their reports made available to all who need them (such as architects and the principal contractor)?			
14. Have any specialist contractors you want to use been checked for their competency?			
15. Have you, as a site manager, been involved in the design for the site set up and therefore instrumental in ensuring overhead and underground services are kept as clear as possible (such as traffic routing around the site and material storage areas)?			

GD15 Underground and overhead services checklist *continued*

Training and competency requirements	Yes	No	N/A
16. Do the workers have the requisite skills for the tasks to be undertaken (are they competent to work at height, have they been briefed on working near overhead services)?			
17. Are CSCS and/or alternative qualification cards required for the project?			
18. Will the barriers and goal posts around the overhead services be checked, ensuring this is done by a competent person?			
19. Have arrangements been made for toolbox talks as required (to update on procedures or to highlight an issue that has arisen on site)?			
Safe systems of work and basic control measures	**Yes**	**No**	**N/A**
20. Have the method statements and risk assessments been submitted and approved prior to contractors commencing on site; are they compatible with the safe system of work contained with the construction phase plan?			
21. Have the workers read and signed the risk assessments and method statements, thereby ensuring they work according to the site's safe system of work?			
22. Is there a feedback system so workers can comment when they feel control measures are unsuitable or inadequate? (This could be an anonymous system.)			
Specific regulatory or special requirements	**Yes**	**No**	**N/A**
23. Are there registers on site for statutory inspections?			
24. Has an emergency plan been prepared (for example, in the case of contact with an overhead service or a gas main being breached, such as fire and/or explosion, serious injuries)?			
25. Has a system been set up for permits to dig and/or permits to work (such as underground services or working in close proximity to overhead services)?			

Further information

- ☑ HSE publication *Avoidance of danger from overhead power lines (GS6)*.
- ☑ National Joint Utilities Group (NJUG) *Guidelines on the positioning and colour coding of underground utilities' apparatus* (latest issue).

Comments

Name		Position		Signature		Date	

GD

GD16 Work in a confined space without entry of persons checklist

Company name		Project title	
Location		Contract no.	

Work in a confined space without entry of persons	*Tick*
1. Ensure that entry into the space is totally prohibited.	
2. Ensure that the isolation of services and processes has been carried out as necessary.	
3. Wash, clean and purge the workplace, as appropriate, for work to be done.	
4. Ensure that there is a safe system of work for the people concerned.	
5. Ensure that other people know that work is going on.	
6. Authorise work to start only on the issue of a permit to work.	
Comments	

Name		Position		Signature		Date	

GD17 Entry into a confined space without breathing apparatus checklist

Company name		Project title	
Location		Contract no.	

Entry into a confined space without breathing apparatus	*Tick*
1. Follow a safe system of work.	
2. Put in place adequate emergency arrangements before work starts, which will also safeguard rescuers.	
3. Initiate a permit to work that includes the requirements of a permit to enter, unless separate permits are raised.	
4. Withdraw the space from service.	
5. Isolate the workplace from electrical, mechanical, chemical, heat and all other sources.	
6. Check that no inward leakage of gas, fumes, steam or liquids is possible.	
7. Clean, drain and purge the workplace, as necessary, for the type of work to be carried out and entry to be made.	
8. Test the atmosphere for oxygen, flammable gas, toxic gas, and so on.	
9. Carefully check any sludge or deposit that may harbour gas, fumes or liquids.	
10. Carry out a COSHH assessment, if necessary.	
11. Arrange for any checking to be carried out remotely.	
12. If necessary, clean, purge and ventilate the workplace again until the atmosphere is safe to enter.	
13. Ensure that all tools and equipment are safe to use in the area.	
14. Check the provision of protective clothing, harnesses, lifelines, rescue equipment and rescue personnel.	
15. Ensure that rescue personnel are trained in the use of the equipment and are capable of using it.	
16. Ensure rescue equipment is available and easy to get to.	
17. Ensure that the fire and rescue service is informed of the location and nature of the work, where appropriate.	
18. If appropriate, ensure that the external emergency rescue services are informed of the location and type of work being carried out.	
19. Brief all personnel on what is to be done and arrange communications.	
20. Issue the permit to work, which authorises entry and fixes a timescale within which the work must be completed.	
21. Constantly monitor the workspace and communications.	
22. If the task is completed within the timescale, advise all concerned, cancel the permit to work and return the space to service.	
23. If the work is not completed in time, withdraw all staff, cancel the permit to work and consider how best to proceed.	

Comments

Name		Position		Signature		Date	

GD

GD18 Entry into a confined space with breathing apparatus checklist

Entry into a confined space with breathing apparatus	*Tick*
1. Follow a safe system of work.	
2. Put in place adequate emergency arrangements before work starts, which will also safeguard rescuers.	
3. Initiate a permit to work.	
4. Withdraw the space from service.	
5. Isolate the workplace from electrical, mechanical, chemical, heat and all other sources.	
6. Check that no inward leakage of gas, steam or liquids is possible.	
7. Clean, drain and purge the workplace, as necessary, for the type of work and entry.	
8. Test the atmosphere for flammable gas, toxic gas, oxygen, and so on.	
9. Decide which type of breathing apparatus is to be used.	
10. Ensure that the personnel involved have a current, valid certificate for the type and use of breathing apparatus.	
11. Ensure that all tools and equipment are safe for use in the work area.	
12. Check the provision of protective clothing, harnesses, lifelines, rescue equipment and rescue personnel.	
13. Ensure that rescue personnel are adequately trained in the use of rescue equipment and they are capable of using it correctly.	
14. Ensure rescue equipment is available and easy to get to.	
15. Ensure that the fire and rescue service is informed of the location and nature of the work.	
16. If appropriate, ensure that the external emergency rescue services are informed of the location and type of work being carried out.	
17. Brief personnel on what is to be done and arrange communications.	
18. Issue the permit to work, which authorises entry and fixes a timescale within which the work must be completed.	
19. Constantly monitor the workspace and communications.	
20. If the task is completed within the timescale, advise all concerned, cancel the permit to work and return the space to service.	
21. If the work is not completed in time, withdraw all staff, cancel the permit to work and consider how best to proceed.	

Comments

Name		Position		Signature		Date	

GD19 Confined space permit

Serial no. CS.........

Company name		**Project title**	
Location		**Contract no.**	

Part 1 – Authorisation by permit co-ordinator

Contractor			Contractor's supervisor		
Permit date		Permit start time		Permit finish time	

Confined space location and description, including any plant or processes

Hazards

The following processes within the confined space have been **withdrawn** from service.

Electrical power		Yes		No	Pressure systems		Yes		No
Mechanical power		Yes		No	Liquids/flowing substances		Yes		No
Relevant isolation permit no.									

There exists the potential for the following hazards to be present.

flammable substances		Yes		No	ingress/presence of liquids		Yes		No
oxygen enrichment/deficiency*		Yes		No	solids that can flow		Yes		No
toxic gases, fumes or vapours		Yes		No	excessive heat or cold*		Yes		No

Activities within confined space

Safe systems

A suitable and sufficient written safe system of work must be produced for this activity.

Risk assessment document no.		**Author**	
Method statement document no.		**Author**	

The risk assessment/method statement* is enclosed with the original permit.		Yes		No

The confined space has been assessed and the following control measures, identified within the written safe system of work, are to be implemented *(tick all that apply)*.

	Removal of residues		Full breathing apparatus (BA)
	Use of intrinsically safe tools		Escape BA only
	Purge atmosphere before entry		First aid/emergency procedures
	Forced ventilation/extraction*		Tools and equipment checked for safe use
	Weil's disease cards issued		System of communication in place (e.g. radios/mobiles)
	Team leader only/rescue team*		Warning signs/barriers in place
	Safety harnesses/lifelines*		Competency of work team checked

Continued atmospheric testing – record unit type/serial no.

Permission is granted to work within the confined space according to the safe systems.

Name		**Position**		**Signature**		**Date**	

Part 2 – Receipt by supervisor

A recorded briefing has been delivered to the workforce on this safe system of work.		Yes		No

As the supervisor, I am familiar with the scope of work and safe systems to be implemented.

Name		**Position**		**Signature**		**Date**	

Part 3 – Completion by supervisor

The activities authorised by this permit have finished and the confined space fully vacated.

Name		**Position**		**Signature**		**Date**	

Part 4 – Cancellation by permit co-ordinator

The confined space and any plant within it, have been returned to service.		Yes		No

The activities authorised by this permit have now ceased. The cancellation of this permit now precludes any further work taking place in this confined space.

Name		**Position**		**Signature**		**Date**	

** Delete as applicable*

(Reproduced by permission of HMSO.)

GD

GD20 Confined space entry RAMS checklist

This risk assessment and method statement (RAMS) checklist must be completed by the competent, nominated person and reviewed by the appointed person before a confined space entry permit can be issued. A copy of the checklist must also be attached to the permit and its findings briefed to all operatives entering the confined space.

Company name		**Project title**	
Location		**Contract no.**	

Confined space entry RAMS			
	Yes	**N/A**	**Comments**
1. Has a risk assessment and method statement been approved?			
2. Are all those entering the confined space trained and competent?			
3. Is the correct personal protective equipment (PPE) identified on the risk assessment, readily available and fit for use?			
4. Is there adequate access and egress?			
5. Is an emergency and rescue plan in place and approved?			
6. Is adequate emergency and rescue equipment in place?			
7. Has the rescue team been trained in its use?			
a) Rescue services informed? Telephone no.			
8. Has a system of communication been established and are emergency contact numbers available?			
a) Confined space supervisor's contact details. Telephone no.			
9. Is there a requirement for forced ventilation to be in place? If so, what type?			
10. Has the atmosphere been monitored prior to entry and the results recorded?			
11. Has the monitoring equipment been calibrated?			
12. Is the monitoring equipment correct (is it capable of detecting gases, lack of oxygen or flammable atmospheres, etc.)?			
13. Have all those entering the space been briefed on the monitoring equipment and what to do in the event of an emergency?			
14. Have all possible harmful substances been removed from the space?			
15. Have all services to the space been isolated or disconnected? If so, who is responsible for continued isolation?			
16. Is breathing apparatus required? If so, what type and is it HSE approved?			
17. If breathing apparatus is required, are all persons competent in its use?			
18. If breathing apparatus is to be used have those entering been face-fit tested?			
19. Are all the necessary signs and barriers available?			
20. Is intrinsically safe task lighting available?			
21. Are any other permits required (such as hot works)?			

Comments							
Name		**Position**		**Signature**		**Date**	

GD

GD21 Entry/access (limitation of access) permit

Company name		Project title	
Location		Contract no.	

Part 1

Reference no.		
Address		
Contractor		
Team completing work	Name	Signature
Competent person supervising the work		
Other members of the team		
Location		

Location entrance(s) must be signed with the notice of access control

Part 2 – Attachments

Risk assessment and method statement		Yes		No	Approved risk assessment and method statement no.	
Checklists		Yes	*(permit will not be approved if checklists not attached)*			

Part 3 – Authorisation

Any special precautions required?	

The persons designated above (and only those persons) are hereby granted permission to enter and work in the controlled location in accordance with the approved risk assessment and method statement.

Permit to commence	Date		Time	
Permit to expire	Date		Time	

This permit cannot cover more than one shift and can only be issued for the maximum of a 12-hour period.

Name		Position		Signature		Date	

Part 4 – Acceptance of permit

I hereby confirm that all persons working within the scope of this permit will be adequately briefed on its content and will abide by the conditions of the permit.

Name		Position		Signature		Date	

Part 5 – Completion of work

The work for which this permit was issued is complete and all persons, materials and equipment under my supervision have been withdrawn.

Name		Position		Signature		Date	

Part 6 – Works complete

I certify that I personally examined the work area detailed above and that the work specified has been satisfactorily completed.

Comments

Name		Position		Signature		Date	

The permit is now cancelled – a new permit will be required if work is to continue.

GD

GD21 Entry/access (limitation of access) permit *continued*

This checklist must be completed by the trade contractor's competent, nominated person and reviewed by the appointed person before a permit can be issued. A copy of the checklist must also be attached to the permit.

***Note:** only questions 3, 4, 6, 7, 8, 11, 14 and 15 can be answered N/A.*

Entry/access permit	Yes	No	N/A	Comments
1. Is there adequate access and egress?				
2. Has a risk assessment and method statement been approved?				
3. Is monitoring equipment required (and if so has it been calibrated)?				
4. Have all harmful substances been removed from the space?				
5. Are all those entering the area trained and competent?				
6. Is a rescue plan in place and approved?				
7. Is adequate rescue equipment in place?				
8. Has the rescue team been trained in its use?				
9. Has a system of communication been established and are emergency contact numbers available?				
10. Have all services to the area been isolated or disconnected?				
11. Is the correct personal protective equipment (PPE) readily available and fit for use?				
12. Are all the necessary signs and barriers available?				
13. Is intrinsically safe task lighting available?				
14. Is there a risk of spark or fire? (*If 'Yes' a hot-work permit is required.*)				
15. If working in riser shafts, lift shafts, roof areas, etc:				
a) is adequate fall prevention in place?				
b) have precautions been taken to avoid falling materials and tools?				
c) has the area been checked for potential fragile surfaces?				

Comments

Name		**Position**		**Signature**		**Date**	

GD

GD22 Dangerous substances safety questionnaire

This questionnaire has been worded so that all the correct answers are '**Yes**'. If you answer '**No**' to any question, perhaps you need to give the matter some more attention.

Company name		Project title	
Location		Contract no.	

Dangerous substances			
General	**Yes**	**No**	**N/A**
1. Has a risk assessment been carried out?			
2. Does it indicate that other methods of managing the situation are required (such as a method statement or permit to work system)?			
3. Have employees been made aware of the significant findings of the risk assessment?			
Storage in the open air	**Yes**	**No**	**N/A**
4. Is the base of the store built of concrete and sloped?			
5. Is there a low level sill surrounding the base?			
6. Is there a ramp for access to the store over the sill?			
7. Is a sump provided to catch any leakages or spillages and is the capacity large enough to contain any leakages or spillages?			
8. Is there a roof or cover over the store to protect the contents from direct sunlight?			
9. Is there an adequate separation distance between the store and adjacent buildings or boundaries?			
10. Are appropriate signs displayed (for example, 'Highly flammable' or 'Flashpoint below 32°C')?			
11. Are the correct fire extinguishers provided and positioned adjacent to the store?			
Storage in buildings	**Yes**	**No**	**N/A**
12. Is the storage building used exclusively for the storage of dangerous substances?			
13. If the store is part of a multi-purpose building, is there adequate fire separation from the rest of the building?			
14. Are appropriate signs displayed (for example, 'Highly flammable' or 'Flashpoint below 32°C')?			
15. Is there a sill across the doorway to prevent leakages or spillages reaching the open air and is the capacity large enough to contain any leakages or spillages?			
16. Is there adequate cross-ventilation at both high and low level?			
17. Is there the required separation distance between the store and adjacent buildings or boundaries?			
Storage at the place of work	**Yes**	**No**	**N/A**
18. Is there a lockable metal cabinet available to store small quantities for daily use?			
19. Is it marked with the appropriate safety signs?			
Decanting	**Yes**	**No**	**N/A**
20. Is decanting done only in the open air or in a fire-resisting building?			
21. Is the decanting located away from any source of heat or ignition?			
22. Are dangerous substances only decanted into small, correctly marked containers with effective closures?			
23. Are funnels correctly used to assist decanting?			
24. Are drip trays positioned to catch any leakages or spillages?			
25. Are suitable absorbents or spill kits available to contain any spillage?			
26. Are metal bins available for used absorbents to be placed in?			
27. Are these bins emptied regularly?			
28. Is contaminated absorbent safely, carefully and properly disposed of?			

GD22 Dangerous substances safety questionnaire *continued*

Use of dangerous substances	Yes	No	N/A
29. Where dangerous substances are used, is adequate ventilation provided?			
30. If there is a need for mechanical extraction, is the electric motor out of the line of discharge of the fumes?			
31. Are there signs stating 'No smoking' or 'Naked lights'?			
32. Are metal waste bins with lids provided for dangerous substances that are no longer required?			
33. Are the correct warning notices provided?			
34. Are serviceable fire extinguishers of the correct type provided and positioned adjacent to the workplace?			
35. Are containers with lids provided for cleaning brushes?			
Spraying	**Yes**	**No**	**N/A**
36. Have the materials in use been clearly identified?			
37. Are the correct precautions in relation to use and storage being observed?			
38. Is the correct spraying equipment being used?			
39. Is the correct protective clothing and equipment, including RPE, being worn?			
40. Are the necessary precautions being taken to avoid all ignition risks?			
41. Are warning notices correctly displayed?			
42. Are barriers in use if necessary?			
43. Are serviceable fire extinguishers of the correct type provided and positioned adjacent to the workplace?			
Empty tanks and containers	**Yes**	**No**	**N/A**
44. Are the necessary precautions being taken against the risk of explosion in storage tanks awaiting demolition or dismantling?			
45. Has an explosive gas-free certificate been obtained prior to any hot work? (Check how long the certificate is valid for.)			
46. Is a permit to work system used when work is being carried out on disused or redundant tanks?			
47. Are authorising permits to work to deal with all the confined space issues being obtained before any entry into a tank is made?			
48. Has thought been given to the possibility of contamination around the tank from leakage or spillage?			
49. Has advice been sought from a competent person before work begins?			
Fire emergency procedures	**Yes**	**No**	**N/A**
50. Are the correct types of fire extinguisher provided and suitably positioned adjacent to the store or workplace?			
51. Have the staff been correctly trained to use them?			
52. Are there procedures to call the FRS?			
53. Is there a telephone available to call the FRS?			
54. Is the address of the site displayed on prominent notices conveniently located in offices and near telephones?			
55. Are suitable absorbents or spill kits available to contain any spillage?			

GD22 Dangerous substances safety questionnaire *continued*

Comments							
Name		**Position**		**Signature**		**Date**	

GD23 LPG safety questionnaire

This questionnaire has been worded so that all the correct answers are '**Yes**'. If you answer '**No**' to any question you may need to give the matter some more attention.

Company name		**Project title**	
Location		**Contract no.**	

LPG safety

Storage	**Yes**	**No**	**N/A**
1. Has a risk assessment been carried out?			
2. Has specialist advice been sought prior to the location of fixed or moveable storage tanks?			
3. Is there the required separation distance between the storage tanks and adjacent buildings or boundaries?			
4. Is the base supporting the tanks level?			
5. Is the base paved or concrete?			
6. Is there a chain-link fence surrounding the tank?			
7. Are there barriers to prevent collision?			
8. Are the correct warning signs displayed?			
9. Are there outward opening exits from the cylinder storage compound?			
10. Are the exits non-self locking?			
11. Is the area kept weed free?			
12. Are all access areas being kept clear?			
13. Are the correct type of fire extinguishers provided?			
14. Are all cylinders stored upright?			
15. Are the LPG cylinders three metres from cylinders containing any other products?			
16. Are cylinders being handled safely?			
17. Is the LPG being grouped in not more than 1,000 kg?			
18. Are there 1.5 metre wide gangways?			
19. Is lighting provided?			
20. Is lighting at least two metres above the tallest stack?			
Transportation	**Yes**	**No**	**N/A**
21. Have drivers received adequate training, as required by law?			
22. Are cylinders transported upright and secured?			
23. Is the vehicle equipped with the correct type of fire extinguisher?			
24. Is the vehicle equipped with a first-aid kit?			
25. Does the vehicle carry suitable warning notices?			
26. If using a closed van, are all gas cylinders off-loaded at the end of each journey?			
Use of LPG cylinders and appliances	**Yes**	**No**	**N/A**
27. Are valve caps and protectors replaced after every use?			
28. Are regulators being handled carefully?			
29. Is the correct size of spanner being used to tighten connections?			
30. Is all equipment (such as hoses and clips) being inspected regularly for leaks?			

GD23 LPG safety questionnaire *continued*

Bitumen boilers and cauldrons	Yes	No	N/A
31. Is a competent person supervising?			
32. Is there a fire extinguisher of the correct type readily available?			
33. Is the boiler or cauldron standing on a non-flammable level base?			
34. Is the cylinder in use with the bitumen boiler or cauldron a minimum of three metres away?			
35. Are any cylinders not in use a minimum of six metres away?			
36. Are hoses inspected regularly for damage or bitumen impregnation?			
37. Are cylinders ice-free when the boiler or cauldron is alight?			
38. Should manifolds coupling two or more cylinders be used?			
39. Are bitumen boilers always attended when alight?			
Hand tools	**Yes**	**No**	**N/A**
40. Are cylinders being used in the upright position?			
41. Are purpose-made trolleys being used for cylinders used in conjunction with cutting equipment?			
42. Are hand tools being used at the manufacturer's recommended operating pressures?			
43. Are connecting hoses being regularly checked for wear and damage?			
44. Are cylinder valves being turned off on the completion of work?			
45. Is there a fire extinguisher of the correct type readily available?			
Site huts and other buildings	**Yes**	**No**	**N/A**
46. Are LPG cylinders, supplying heaters and other appliances, fixed outside the building?			
47. Is the gas fed into the building by the provision of fixed copper piping?			
48. Are fixed installations only installed, modified and tested by a Gas Safe registered engineer?			
49. Is the final, short flexible hose as short as possible?			
50. Are all pipes in use easy to get to for inspection?			
51. Is there plenty of ventilation at high and low levels?			
52. Are weekly inspections being carried out on all appliances?			
53. Is there a fire extinguisher of the correct type readily available?			
Fire precautions	**Yes**	**No**	**N/A**
54. Are written procedures provided and displayed prominently?			
55. Is there a telephone available to summon the FRS?			
56. Are the correct types of fire extinguishers provided?			
57. Are your staff trained in the use of fire extinguishers?			
58. Are your staff and visitors aware of the site emergency evacuation alarm and procedure?			
59. Are personnel aware of pressure relief valves?			
60. Are product data sheets available?			

Comments							
Name		**Position**		**Signature**		**Date**	

GD

GE

Environment

The contents of this chapter should be read and used in conjunction with guidance contained within Section E.

Contents

GE01 Resource efficiency and responsible sourcing checklist

Company name		**Project title**	
Location		**Contract no.**	

Resource efficiency and responsible sourcing

	Yes	No	N/A
1. Has the site considered alternative techniques for the efficient use of resources (such as off-site manufacture, design to fit modular sizes, manufacture to fit design and design for disassembly)?			
2. Has the design taken into account the reuse of reprocessed demolition materials or the use of recycled aggregate or excavated soil and materials as part of the site waste management plan?			
3. Are there procedures in place to identify and order the correct type and quantity of materials?			
4. Are there procedures in place to ensure the main materials are sourced responsibly (such as sustainable timber) and records maintained for traceability purposes?			
5. Are deliveries being inspected to avoid damage during unloading, deliveries to wrong area of the site or accepting incorrect specification or quantity?			
6. Are stockpiles and material storage areas away from traffic routes to prevent accidental damage?			
7. Are materials being stored to prevent repetitive handling?			
8. Are materials being stored with the appropriate security to prevent loss, theft or vandalism?			
9. Are stockpiled materials being stored to prevent cross-contamination with other materials or wastes?			
10. Are stockpiled materials being stored away from sensitive areas, drains or watercourses?			
11. Are materials being handled with the correct equipment to prevent accidental damage?			
12. Are hazardous/COSHH materials being stored, issued and disposed of correctly?			

Comments

Name		**Position**		**Signature**		**Date**	

GE

GE02 Waste management, storage and disposal checklist

Company name		Project title	
Location		Contract no.	

Waste management, storage and disposal			
	Yes	No	N/A
1. Has a site waste management plan been prepared, identifying waste types and quantities for the project?			
a) Is it being maintained/updated?			
2. Has a waste target and any relevant objectives been set for the project?			
3. Have the project waste requirements been included in the contracts with trade contractors and suppliers?			
4. Are the project waste requirements included in the site induction?			
5. Have waste responsibilities been defined to know who is disposing of what and when?			
6. Have designated area(s) been established on site to segregate and reuse waste materials?			
7. Have recycling facilities been established to segregate office/canteen wastes (such as paper, cans and plastics)?			
8. Has the site been registered for hazardous waste with the relevant environment agency?			
9. Are waste management permits, licences or exemptions in place for any processing of waste on site (such as crushing and soil treatment)?			
10. Is the WRAP quality protocol being complied with for the production of aggregates from waste?			
11. Is the CL:AIRE Code of Practice being complied with for the treatment and use of contaminated soils (such as appointment of qualified person, materials management plan, and so on)?			
12. Are hazardous wastes (oil, fuel, paints, and so on) collected and stored separately from general wastes?			
13. Is the burning of rubbish on site prohibited, unless a permit/licence has been obtained?			
14. Are registered waste carriers used to remove waste from site and are these checked on a regular basis?			
15. Does the tip where the waste is taken have a licence for the type of waste?			
16. Do waste transfer documents include the right information (six-digit waste codes, licence number of carrier, tip location and declaration regarding the waste hierarchy)?			
17. Are waste transfer documents being retained: two years for non-hazardous and three years for hazardous waste?			

Comments

Name		Position		Signature		Date	

GE

GE03 Energy and transport checklist

Company name		**Project title**	
Location		**Contract no.**	

Energy and transport	Yes	No	N/A
1. Have energy objectives and targets been set for the project?			
2. Has an energy monitoring process been implemented to monitor and report energy consumption and carbon emissions, including business travel and transport?			
3. Have discussions with energy supplier(s) been made to ensure electrical supplies are connected at the earliest opportunity to avoid power from generators?			
4. Have site offices been fitted with practical, energy-saving devices, including low energy lighting (LED), passive infrared sensors for lighting, timer switches and thermostats for heating, hot water, and so on?			
5. Does the site induction cover the main energy efficiency issues (such as maintaining plant and switching off when not in use)?			
6. Are there signs in place advising site personnel to switch equipment off when not required?			
7. Is site office equipment set up to print efficiently (such as double-sided) and to a central location rather than individual printers?			
8. Has the site considered renewable energy to contribute to powering the site accommodation?			
9. Is there a logistics/transport plan that considers efficient transport arrangements (such as the use of consolidation centres or just-in-time delivery)?			
10. Have quality checks on the installed fabric insulation been completed?			
11. Did the building meet its target airtightness level?			
12. Have all renewable energy systems (such as biomass or PV) been fully commissioned and tested?			
13. Have all building services, meters and control systems been fully commissioned and tested?			
14. Is a plan in place for post occupancy monitoring and seasonal commissioning?			
15. Have local, sensitive areas been identified (such as schools and residents)?			
16. Has the site considered green travel arrangements for reducing staff travel to site (such as rail and water)?			
17. Has the location of suitable parking arrangements for private cars and plant been defined?			
18. Has permission been obtained from the Local Authority for any road closures or erection of hoarding on the public highway?			
19. Have local pedestrian diversion routes been agreed with the Local Authority?			
20. Have delivery routes for construction traffic been agreed with the Local Authority?			
21. Have suppliers been made aware of any delivery restrictions and routes?			
22. Are entrance and exit gates on main roads rather than side roads?			
23. Are deliveries scheduled to avoid traffic disruption or queuing outside of the site?			
24. Are delivery vehicles switched off when being loaded and unloaded (unless needed to operate a Hiab or similar)?			
25. Have designated vehicle routes on site been defined?			
26. Are deliveries organised to avoid excessive use of reversing sirens?			
27. Would it be possible to use eco-friendly site cabins?			
28. Have the designers specified using low carbon concrete?			
29. Would it be possible to source materials from local suppliers?			

Comments

Name		**Position**		**Signature**		**Date**	

GE04 Water management and pollution prevention checklist

Company name		**Project title**	
Location		**Contract no.**	

Water management and pollution prevention

	Yes	No	N/A
1. Have all watercourses and drainage systems been identified on site?			
2. Have all works in, above or near to watercourses been agreed with the relevant Flood Defence Authority (Local Authority or regulatory body, in the case of statutory main rivers)?			
3. Have all discharges to streams, ditches and drainage systems been consented to by the relevant environment agency?			
4. Have all water abstractions from rivers, ponds, lakes or water mains been consented to by the relevant environment agency?			
5. Are site personnel inducted and suitably trained in dealing with waste water on site?			
6. Have water monitoring procedures been put in place to ensure discharges are the correct quality?			
7. Have water discharges been properly treated (such as using settlement tanks or lagoons)?			
8. Have designated areas been defined to wash out concrete lorries away from watercourses and drains?			
9. Are watercourses and drainage systems protected from run-off and silty water?			
10. Are all fuel tanks effectively bunded to at least 110% of their capacity (or 25% of total capacity for drums)?			
11. Are all oil and diesel tanks and chemicals located as far as possible from drains and watercourses?			
12. Are oil and diesel tanks separated from the ground by an impermeable layer?			
13. Are all oil and diesel tanks and chemicals marked with the type of contents, volume and appropriate hazard warning signs?			
14. Are steps being taken on site to prevent ground contamination or pollution by fuels, oils, chemicals, paint, and so on?			
15. Have site personnel been made aware of the site spillage response procedures through inductions and toolbox talks?			
16. Are appropriate spill kits available and appropriate personnel trained to deal with any accidental spillages to drains or watercourses?			
17. Have proactive measures been taken to reduce water consumption (such as grey water recycling) and water saving devices (such as waterless urinals)?			
18. Is water consumption being monitored and recorded and communicated to site personnel to promote water minimisation?			

Comments

Name		**Position**		**Signature**		**Date**	

GE

GE05 Statutory nuisance checklist

Company name		**Project title**	
Location		**Contract no.**	

Statutory nuisance

	Yes	No	N/A
1. Has the appropriate liaison or communication taken place with local stakeholders that may be affected by nuisance?			
2. Are appropriate dust suppression techniques used to minimise air pollution from timber sawing or planing, stone or block cutting, crushing, and so on?			
3. Is dust on site haul roads and material stockpiles dampened down adequately on dry, windy days?			
4. Are haul roads located away from sensitive areas (such as rivers and ditches)?			
5. Are site vehicle speed limits controlled to reduce dust?			
6. Are public roads regularly cleaned using a road sweeper or vacuum?			
7. Do vehicles that remove granular or dusty materials have sheeted covers?			
8. Are all plant and vehicles in good working order with an up to date maintenance or service log?			
9. Are enclosed chutes and covered skips used for lowering dusty demolition or waste materials?			
10. Are cement and concrete being mixed in enclosed areas to prevent dust?			
11. Are material stockpiles or spoil heaps stored away from sensitive areas (such as drains, rivers and ditches)?			
12. Have the works been assessed to identify the noise and vibration impact on local neighbours?			
13. Has the local environmental health officer and neighbours been consulted and forewarned of any out-of-hours or major disruptive activities?			
14. If a Control of Pollution Act Section 61 consent is required, are noise levels being recorded to ensure that levels are kept within limits?			
15. If possible, have working methods been reviewed to use equipment that reduces noise and vibration (such as pile jacking and chemical bursting)?			
16. Have working hours been defined to restrict noisy operations to certain times of day?			
17. Is noisy plant kept as far as possible from sensitive receptors?			
18. Are deliveries planned to suit the local area?			
19. Are haul routes well maintained to prevent vehicle noise and vibration?			
20. Where required, are noise screens being used to reduce noise transmission?			
21. Are noise screens and hoarding well maintained with no holes and gaps?			
22. Has lighting been positioned to avoid a nuisance at night and is non-essential lighting switched off at night?			
23. Does the site have a procedure for dealing with complaints and issues?			

Comments

Name		**Position**		**Signature**		**Date**	

GE06 Ecology checklist

Company name		Project title	
Location		Contract no.	

Ecology

	Yes	No	N/A
1. Has the contractual and client documentation been reviewed to identify all sensitive areas containing wildlife?			
2. Have all relevant ecological risks been included in the construction environmental management plan, together with their mitigation measures?			
3. Have licences been obtained from Natural England or the relevant conservation body to move protected species or disrupt their habitats (such as bats, badgers and lizards)?			
4. Have specific bio-security plans been worked up and implemented if native species have been identified?			
5. Are areas containing wildlife suitably protected from the construction work?			
6. Are trees suitably protected to avoid damage from the works?			
7. Have vegetation removal works been programmed to avoid breeding and nesting periods?			
8. Has permission been given by the Local Authority to remove hedges or trees that have a tree preservation order?			
9. Has approval been given by the relevant environment agency to deal with invasive plants (such as Japanese knotweed and giant hogweed)?			
10. Has approval been given by the relevant environment agency for the treatment or management of plants adjacent to a watercourse?			
11. Do treatment operatives hold the appropriate qualification and certificate of competency for the use of pesticides?			

Comments

Name		Position		Signature		Date	

GE07 Contaminated land checklist

Company name		Project title	
Location		Contract no.	

Contaminated land	Yes	No	N/A
1. Has a preliminary or desktop investigation been carried out of the site and its previous uses to identify the risks from contamination?			
2. Has a site investigation been carried out to identify the type and extent of any suspected contamination?			
3. Are the testing company and laboratory suitably competent to carry out the testing and analysis of any contamination?			
4. Has the proposed remediation strategy been agreed by the local planning authority and relevant environment agency, where appropriate?			
5. Does the site induction cover details of contamination and the procedures for working in areas of known contamination?			
6. Are there procedures in place to ensure that work is stopped and appropriate reporting takes place if contamination is accidently discovered or disturbed?			
7. Are areas of contamination fenced off to prevent vehicles and plant spreading the contamination across the site?			
8. Are relevant environmental permits in place for the treatment and remediation of contamination?			
9. Are suitable controls in place for dealing with contaminated water (such as discharge consents to foul sewers or tanker)?			
10. If contaminated materials have to be stockpiled, are they covered to prevent run-off and wind-blown contamination?			
11. Are contaminated materials stored on hard-stand areas to avoid contamination of ground and groundwater below?			
12. Are stockpiles positioned well away from drainage systems or watercourses?			
13. Are there suitable wheel-washing facilities to clean contaminated vehicles before leaving site?			
14. Where vehicles remove contaminated materials, are they covered with sheets before leaving site?			

Comments

Name		Position		Signature		Date	

GE

GE08 Archaeology and heritage checklist

Company name		Project title	
Location		Contract no.	

Archaeology and heritage

	Yes	No	N/A
1. Has the contract documentation been reviewed to determine the presence or location of archaeology or protected heritage and buildings?			
2. Have designers been involved to integrate known archaeological features into the project?			
3. Have licences or permissions been obtained to carry out work on or around archaeology or protected heritage and buildings?			
4. Where there are works on or around known archaeology or heritage, has a watching brief or specialist been employed to monitor and record the works?			
5. Have locations containing archaeology or heritage been adequately fenced off or protected?			
6. Have suitable communication arrangements been put in place for unknown finds that may be discovered, and for reporting these to the local archaeological officer or Local Authority, and recorded?			

Comments

Name		Position		Signature		Date	

GE

GE09 Site environment management systems checklist

Company name		Project title	
Location		Contract no.	

Site environment management systems

	Yes	No	N/A
1. Is the company (or site) environmental policy available and displayed on site, with relevant requirements highlighted at the site induction?			
2. Has the contract and client documentation been reviewed to identify the site-specific environmental requirements, including planning conditions?			
3. Has a construction environmental management plan been prepared to identify the relevant targets, objectives, issues and controls?			
4. Is there a system for ensuring that suitable and sufficient arrangements are in place for the management, storage and disposal of waste through the production of a site waste management plan?			
5. Is there a system for ensuring that all site personnel (including sub-contractors) are made aware of the project environmental issues and standards through site inductions, briefings and toolbox talks?			
6. Have responsibilities for environmental management been defined and communicated through inductions, noticeboards, and so on?			
7. Is someone responsible for ensuring that environmentally sensitive areas are identified and protected (such as drains, rivers, streams, groundwater and areas containing protected plants and animals)?			
8. Is there a system for ensuring that the necessary environmental licences have been identified and granted (such as discharges of water and effluent, tree preservation orders, premises producing hazardous waste and waste management licences)?			
9. Is there a system for ensuring that method statements include sufficient control measures for environmental management?			
10. Is there a system for sites to deal with environmental emergencies (such as for spillages and groundwater contamination) and for notifying them to the relevant authority?			
11. Is there a suitable and sufficient monitoring regime in place to ensure that the site environmental requirements are being met (such as relevant environmental inspections for oil and waste storage, protected areas, water quality, noise and dust)?			
12. Are environmental records being maintained (such as waste transfer notes, consignment notes, noise and water monitoring)?			
13. Have adequate arrangements been established for liaison and communication with local stakeholders (residents, shops, businesses, schools and parish council)?			

Comments

Name		Position		Signature		Date	

GE10 Environment objectives and targets

Objective	Action	Key performance indicator/target	Performance*			
			Q1	Q2	Q3	Q4
Water Monitor site water usage and aim for a reduction in usage against previous year baseline Offices to identify their usage and identify ways to reduce water demand	■ Sites to continue measuring and reporting on site water usage. (All sites to fit flow meters or utilise existing meters) ■ Projects to identify and implement water saving measures on site ■ Advertise and raise awareness of water efficiency through newsletters and communications ■ On design and build projects, teams are to identify and communicate stakeholder risks and opportunities presented by water use	All projects to report on water usage				
		Projects to identify and implement water saving efficiencies to reduce company usage of water by 5% against previous year's consumption figures/£100k turnover				
		All offices to identify and install water-saving efficiencies				
		Communicate risks and opportunities presented by water to identified clients				
Energy and carbon reduction Monitor energy usage on sites and offices to reduce company energy usage by 5% against previous year baseline	■ Install sub-meters in all offices to record energy usage ■ Promote energy and carbon awareness through training and promotional events ■ All offices to prepare a transport and logistics plan ■ All offices to create a green travel plan ■ Each office to measure the carbon footprint of projects where this has been requested by the client ■ Identify suitable sites for carbon footprint assessment	All new projects and offices to have meters installed (Kwh/100 m^2)				
		Each office to create a green travel plan				
		Each office to receive an energy audit and implement energy saving measures				
		Measure the carbon footprint of projects where this has been requested by the client				

*** Key:** 1 Completed/target met; 2 Started/near target; 3 Not started/not on target

GE

GE10 Environment objectives and targets *continued*

Objective	Action	Key performance indicator/target	Performance*			
			Q1	Q2	Q3	Q4
Responsible sourcing Monitor the use of responsibly sourced timber	▪ Projects to procure timber in accordance with Government's CPET requirements where possible ▪ Projects to identify and implement the use of recycled aggregates/materials, where possible	All projects to report on the percentage (by value) of all site timber having chain of custody				
		All projects to report on volume of recycled aggregates				
Waste Reduce waste production in line with the waste hierarchy and raise waste awareness through training	▪ Set waste reduction targets based on previous year's data ▪ Identify and develop good practice for waste reduction ▪ Undertake supply chain waste reduction workshops ▪ All sites to appoint a waste champion ▪ Project staff to receive SWMP refresher training.	Company to divert at least 85% of construction waste from landfill				
		Sites to reduce waste produced on site by 5% compared to previous year's levels				
Biodiversity Improve company knowledge on biodiversity issues and benefits whilst improving the biodiversity on our sites	▪ Deliver appropriate biodiversity training to teams ▪ Benchmark and improve the biodiversity on projects where relevant (such as BREEAM, client) ▪ Share good practice examples	Deliver relevant awareness training (identified on a project, risk basis)				
		Projects to identify ways to improve the biodiversity on site				
Environmental accident rate Ensure all site personnel are aware of environmental incident reporting requirements	▪ Ensure all sites record environmental incidents, near misses and complaints ▪ Encourage dialogue on environmental issues/situations that are not easy to implement, are misunderstood or ignored ▪ Include environmental incident/near miss reporting within site inductions and toolbox talks	Target a continued zero incident rate				
		All risk assessments and method statements to include specific environmental risks				
		Toolbox talks – environmental topic ratio 1:4				
Community engagement Increase communication with local communities and maintain a considerate constructor approach	▪ Capture and collate in an annual report all the community engagement work the company and projects carry out ▪ Create a company community engagement plan ▪ Improve compliance with Considerate Constructors' scheme (CCS) by creating a company minimum standard for sites, share good practice and have a dedicated CCS folder for each registered site	Record any community engagement work and send to the environmental team/advisor or head office				
		Each project to have a CCS folder and a target score of 34				

* **Key:** 1 Completed/target met   2 Started/near target   3 Not started/not on target

GF

Specialist activities

The contents of this chapter should be read and used in conjunction with guidance contained within Section F.

Contents

GF01 Working on the highway competency checklist

Company name		**Project title**	
Location		**Contract no.**	

Overview

What you need to know

Due to the proximity of the travelling public, and to a lesser degree construction plant, carrying out construction at road works can be disproportionately hazardous, as reflected in the rising number of accidents at road works. The Highways Agency and the Highways Term Maintenance Association are working together to improve the situation.

What you need to do

If you do not already carry out work on the highway but intend to do so, you must ensure that your workers gain the appropriate qualifications and competencies before you bid for work.

You must familiarise yourself with the:

- ☑ hazards and significant risks arising out of working on the highway so that you can compile meaningful risk assessments and method statements
- ☑ requirements for signage and other traffic management equipment
- ☑ different standards of high-visibility clothing required.

Significant hazards and risks

Safety	**Yes**	**No**	**N/A**
1. Has the proximity of moving road traffic and construction plant been considered?			
2. Have general safety hazards (such as excavations, manual handling, working at height, and so on) been taken into account?			
Health	**Yes**	**No**	**N/A**
3. Is there noise and vibration from adjacent traffic and construction plant?			
4. Is there a chance of skin contact with hazardous substances?			
Environment	**Yes**	**No**	**N/A**
5. Is there a risk of land contamination through use of substances and disposal of waste?			
6. Is dust likely to be created by groundworks, cutting or drilling activities?			
Managerial/supervisory tasks (including pre-planning)	**Yes**	**No**	**N/A**
7. Have specific hazards been identified and consideration given on how to eliminate or reduce the risks?			
8. Have the significant findings of the risk assessment and the method statement been communicated to the workforce? (Review and update both as necessary and communicate any changes.)			
Training/competency requirements	**Yes**	**No**	**N/A**
9. Is the site manager or supervisor New Roads and Street Work Act (NRSWA) qualified?			
10. Is the banksman, who will be controlling plant movements, qualified?			
Safe systems of work/basic control measures	**Yes**	**No**	**N/A**
11. Has work been planned and organised in accordance with the requirements of the Code of Practice to the NRSWA?			
12. Has work been planned and organised in accordance with further Highways Agency guidance?			
Specific regulatory or special requirements	**Yes**	**No**	**N/A**
13. Has the safety of road users, including pedestrians, been ensured through effective signage?			
14. Has the health and safety of all workers been ensured through thorough planning and strong management?			

Further information

- ☑ The Code of Practice to the New Roads and Street Works Act (often referred to as the *Red book*).

GF01 Working on the highway competency checklist *continued*

Comments

Name		Position		Signature		Date	

GF02 Point of work risk assessment

Point of work risk assessment			
Company name			
Project title		Location	
Contract no.		Date	

Part 1. Stop

Before you start	Yes	No	N/A
Are you at the correct site, item of plant or location?			
Do you have the right documentation for the job?			
Do you have the right PPE for the job?			
Are power tools and leads and plant tested?			
Are scaffolds and ladders inspected (access safe)?			
Is lifting equipment inspected?			

If you have answered 'No' to any of the above, take the required action or report to your supervisor. If in doubt always ask!

Part 2. Think

Safety and health assessment *(If the hazard is present tick the box)*

	Falls from height		Entry into a confined space		Poor lighting
	Falling or flying objects		Dust		Temperature (high/low)
	Chemicals or harmful substances		Fumes		Adverse weather
	Heat, fire or explosion		Noise		Uncertified equipment
	Asphyxiation or drowning		Vibration		Risk to you from your work
	Risk to plant		Electricity		Risk to others from your work
	Contact with stationary object		Residues		Stored energy or insecure load
	Object overturning or collapsing		Underground services		Traffic or moving vehicles
	Slips, trips or falls on the same level		Manual handling		Other *(state)*

If required, you must have a rescue plan in place. Provide brief details.
(You must always be able to provide a way of safe escape in the event of something going wrong.)

If no control measures are in place for the hazards identified above, then Part 3 (on the next page) needs to be completed and appropriate control measures put in place before work commences.

GF02 Point of work risk assessment *continued*

Part 3. Act

Additional safety assessment

Hazard *(identified overleaf)*	**Control measures or precautions**	**Remaining risk**		
		High	**Medium**	**Low**

Part 4. Review

End of job review

Are there any lessons for next time?		Yes		No	
Has the work created any new hazards?		Yes		No	

If you have answered 'Yes' to either of these questions, make a brief note below and tell your supervisor.

Lessons learnt and future site or location visit advice *(list here any information that would make the next visit safer and include contact details if appropriate)*

Risk assessment briefing							
Name		**Position**		**Signature**		**Date**	

GF

GF03 Mobile workforce checklist

Company name		Project title	
Location		Contract no.	

Overview

What you need to know

In order to provide mobile workers, including lone and out-of-hours workers, with a safe working environment, means of getting to and from it, suitable welfare facilities and the appropriate tools and materials for the job, planning and a risk assessment must be undertaken before work begins.

What you need to do

Prepare a risk assessment whilst considering what resources are needed to complete the job safely. Liaise with workers and others involved, ensuring all hazards are identified and suitable controls implemented to eliminate or reduce the risks.

Significant hazards and risks

Safety	Yes	No	N/A
1. Can it be a safe working area with pedestrians and vehicles segregated?			
2. Is temporary traffic lighting and street signage needed?			
3. Is there a secure working area with material storage and waste area?			
4. Is there adequate access to and egress from the area in the event of an emergency?			
5. Is there a suitable fire emergency plan, sounder, fire extinguishers and communications?			
6. If a lone worker, is the work suitable for one person alone (such as manual handling)?			
Health	**Yes**	**No**	**N/A**
7. Has an adequate risk assessment been prepared for the tasks to be undertaken?			
8. Have welfare facilities been provided or arranged with the client?			
9. Are there any hazardous substances being used – COSHH?			
10. Has a member of the group received first-aid training?			
11. Has a suitable first-aid kit been provided and information on reporting of accidents?			
Environment	**Yes**	**No**	**N/A**
12. Are there any watercourses nearby?			
13. Does any wildlife need to be considered?			
14. Is there potentially contaminated land?			
15. Is there a potential for contamination by the work activity (such as provision of spill kits)?			
Managerial/supervisory tasks (including pre-planning)	**Yes**	**No**	**N/A**
16. Is there a suitable and sufficient planned scheme of work for what is proposed?			
17. Have the risk assessments been reviewed and found to be task or site specific?			
18. Has the correct transport and equipment been provided?			
19. Have welfare facilities been arranged for the site or arranged with the client?			
20. Have the workers got adequate PPE and any additional equipment (such as goggles or dust masks)?			

GF03 Mobile workforce checklist *continued*

Training/competency requirements	Yes	No	N/A
21. Do the workers have the requisite skills for the tasks to be undertaken (are they competent)?			
22. Are CSCS or similar qualification cards required for the project?			
23. Who is available to give toolbox talks?			
24. Will the works undergo a safety inspection during their operation?			
Safe systems of work/basic control measures	**Yes**	**No**	**N/A**
25. Has a point of work risk assessment been completed?			
26. Is there a procedure to update documentation during the works?			
27. Are employees empowered to take action if additional control measures are needed?			
Specific regulatory or special requirements	**Yes**	**No**	**N/A**
28. Are contact information and safeguards in place for lone workers?			
29. If necessary, is a rescue plan in place (such as for rescue from a trench)?			
Further information			
☑ HSE publication *Provision of welfare facilities during construction work* (CIS59).			
☑ HSE publication *Working alone, health and safety guidance on the risks of lone working* (INDG73).			
Comments			

Name		Position		Signature		Date	

GF04 Working over or near to water

Ready for a rescue?

Company name		Project title	
Location		Contract no.	

Overview
What you need to know
The skills and equipment that will be necessary for rescuing someone from the water, with regard to the prevailing circumstances on site.
What you need to do
Put a rescue management plan in place and ensure it is communicated to, and understood by, anyone who is at risk of accidental entry into the water. Provide the equipment and training necessary.

Significant hazards and risks			
Safety	**Yes**	**No**	**N/A**
1. Is there a risk of drowning due to any number of factors?			
2. Is there a risk of serious injuries resulting from impact with the structure during a fall?			
Health	**Yes**	**No**	**N/A**
3. Could Leptospirosis (Weil's disease) be contracted from ingesting contaminated water?			
4. Has the ingestion of other contaminants in the water been considered?			
5. Is there a risk of catching hypothermia from being in cold water for too long?			
6. Is there a risk of suspension trauma from being left suspended in a harness for too long?			
Environment	**Yes**	**No**	**N/A**
7. Are petrol or diesel closely controlled when refuelling rescue craft?			
Managerial/supervisory tasks (including pre-planning)	**Yes**	**No**	**N/A**
8. Have measures been provided to prevent falls?			
9. Where falls are possible have lifejackets and training been provided and their correct use monitored?			
10. Has the appropriate rescue equipment been selected and maintained as necessary?			
11. Have the people at risk been trained on how to avoid falling into the water and what to do if they do?			
Training/competency requirements	**Yes**	**No**	**N/A**
12. Have the workers been given general safe working at height guidance?			
13. Has additional training been provided for safety boat operators and crew (RYA trained)?			
14. Are qualified first aiders (HSE-accredited trained) available?			
Safe systems of work/basic control measures	**Yes**	**No**	**N/A**
15. Are safe working practices at height in place to avoid a rescue being necessary?			
16. Are procedures in place to ensure the prompt location and rescue of anyone who is in the water?			
17. Are the emergency services immediately contacted if it is obvious that expert medical assistance is needed?			
Specific regulatory or special requirements	**Yes**	**No**	**N/A**
18. Do management and workers comply with the Work at Height Regulations?			
19. Is personal flotation equipment and other PPE provided as necessary?			

GF04 Working over or near to water *continued*

Further information
☑ HSE information sheet *Personal buoyancy equipment on inland and inshore waters* (AIS1).
Comments

Name		Position		Signature		Date	